Small Building Works Management

Macmillan Building and Surveying Series

Series Editor: Ivor H. Seeley

Emeritus Professor, Nottingham Polytechnic

Advanced Building Measurement, second edition Ivor H. Seeley
Advanced Valuation Diane Butler and David Richmond
An Introduction to Building Services Christopher A. Howard
Applied Valuation Diane Butler
Asset Valuation Michael Rayner
Building Economics, third edition Ivor H. Seeley
Building Maintenance, second edition Ivor H. Seeley
Building Procurement Alan E. Turner
Building Quantities Explained, fourth edition Ivor H. Seeley
Building Surveys, Reports and Dilapidations Ivor H. Seeley
Building Technology, fourth edition Ivor H. Seeley
Civil Engineering Contract Administration and Control Ivor H. Seeley
Civil Engineering Quantities, fourth edition Ivor H. Seeley
Civil Engineering Specification, second edition Ivor H. Seeley
Computers and Quantity Surveyors A. J. Smith
Contract Planning and Contract Procedures, third edition B. Cooke
Contract Planning Case Studies B. Cooke
Design–Build Explained D. E. L. Janssens
Development Site Evaluation N. P. Taylor
Environmental Science in Building, third edition R. McMullan
Housing Associations Helen Cope
Housing Management – Changing Practice Edited by Christine Davies
Information and Technology Applications in Commercial Property, R. Feenan
and T. J. Dixon (Editors)
Introduction to Valuation D. Richmond
Marketing and Property People Owen Bevan
Principles of Property Investment and Pricing W. D. Fraser
Property Valuation Techniques David Isaac and Terry Steley
Public Works Engineering Ivor H. Seeley
Quality Assurance in Building Alan Griffith
Recreation Planning and Development Neil Ravenscroft
Structural Detailing, second edition P. Newton
Urban Land Economics and Public Policy, fourth edition P. N. Balchin,
J. L. Kieve and G. H. Bull
Urban Renewal – Theory and Practice Chris Couch
1980 JCT Standard Form of Building Contract, second edition R. F. Fellows

Series Standing Order

If you would like to receive future titles in this series as they are published, you can make use of our standing order facility. To place a standing order please contact your bookseller or, in case of difficulty, write to us at the address below with your name and address and the name of the series. Please state with which title you wish to begin your standing order. (If you live outside the United Kingdom we may not have the rights for your area, in which case we will forward your order to the publisher concerned.)

Customer Services Department, Macmillan Distribution Ltd
Houndmills, Basingstoke, Hampshire, RG21 2XS, England.

Small Building Works Management

Alan Griffith

M.Sc., Ph.D., MCIOB, FFB, MBIM

MACMILLAN

© Alan Griffith 1992

First published 1992 by
THE MACMILLAN PRESS LTD
Houndmills, Basingstoke, Hampshire RG21 2XS
and London
Companies and representatives
throughout the world

ISBN 0–333–56644–0 hardcover
ISBN 0–333–56645–9 paperback

A catalogue record for this book is available from the British Library

Typeset by Ponting–Green Publishing Services, Sunninghill, Berks

Printed in Hong Kong

To Michela

Contents

Acknowledgements

My appreciation is extended to the following persons:

- Colin W. Campbell, who kindly permitted me to refer to his Master's Degree research work.
- Jeremy D. Headley, Research Associate, Heriot-Watt University, who is further developing on-going research into small building works management.
- Professor Ivor H. Seeley, the Series Editor, for reading through and commenting extensively on the draft typescript.
- Mrs Elasaid McLean for producing the text, graphics and diagrammatical information for this book.

Preface

Small works are an established and vital part of the construction economy; they account for a growing proportion of construction output and are prominent in each and every sector of the construction industry, none more so than in building. Small building works are so often understated, yet there can be no doubt that they require professional procurement, organisation and management if their undertaking is to be successful and cost effective. Whilst the principles involved parallel those of other building activities, the management tools, techniques and procedures must be matched to the nature and scale of the particular project.

There may be much room for improvement in the ways that clients procure and contractors carry out small building works. The diversity of methods and procedures used and the absence of widely accepted guide-lines serve to highlight this clearly. Procedures chosen may be more often than not based upon ease of administration rather than efficiency and cost effectiveness. To be carried out successfully, small building works must be actively managed.

The wide diversity of activity seen in small building works may encompass repair, maintenance, alteration, refurbishment and a wide range of 'retrofit' activities in addition to new build works. This diversity is also represented in the value of small works which may range from minor work costing but a few hundred pounds to extensive contracts running into millions of pounds and in the technical complexity of the work, which may range from simple semi-skilled trade tasks to highly complex construction projects.

This book sets out to provide a detailed guide to the principles and practices of small building works management. Chapter 1 introduces small building works, identifying their significance and importance within con-struction output. It should be appreciated when reading this chapter that the construction industry statistics referred to in the text and reflected in all the figures are 1989 compilations, published in 1991. Chapter 2 identifies different types of small works, those with jobbing characteristics, ordered works and small/minor building projects. Chapter 3 considers the relation-ship between the client and contractor, considering the client's choice of direct labour or contractor, selection of contractor and assessment of risk. Chapters 4 and 5 describe the various ways of procuring small works through works orders, daywork term contracts and lump-sum approaches and identifies applicable forms of contract. Chapter 6 reviews both the client's and contractor's organisations and management of small building works, examining the control mechanisms for time, cost and quality. Chapters 7 and 8 identify the difficulties and problems experienced in small building works management and considers appropriate action for potential improvement.

The professional management of small building works is emphasised throughout this book. Although often misperceived as a poor relation to other types of building projects, clients and contractors must recognise the true worth and importance of small building works. To this end, this book provides a valuable text/reference for construction professionals, clients and contractors in both the public and private sectors.

1 Introduction

1.1 Construction output and building industry trends

General

Estimated statistics, published in 1991,[1] indicate that the UK's Gross Capital Stock of Buildings and Works approximates to £2285 billion (at 1991 prices), with almost seventy-two per cent of this total representing the stock of buildings. This proportion is, essentially, the value of buildings which require to be maintained on an annual basis in order to facilitate their continual effective use. As a proportion of the Gross Capital Stock of Buildings and Works, only a somewhat minuscule proportion, on average 1.56 per cent per annum over the last decade, has been spent on their repair and maintenance. This figure is however, somewhat deceptive. In monetary terms, of the £46.2 billion construction industry output in 1989, £19 billion or forty-one per cent was actually spent on the repair and maintenance sector of the construction industry. The value of repair and maintenance to the Gross Capital Stock of Buildings and Works is, in economic terms, substantial.

From a social perspective, the capital building stock is a vital and integral part of the built environment. Renewal and expansion of the building stock represents the foundation of and framework for the generation of improved infrastructure and development of new communities. The emphasis that is placed upon the maintenance of existing buildings and development of new stock has considerable significance upon the way that people perceive, utilise and treat that facility and this, in turn, greatly determines the general quality of life, at home and at work.

The upkeep of buildings and works in both the public and private sector depends, to a large extent, not just upon the policy of national and local government and the private procurement of building and related work by major clients, but also upon the public. Householders themselves make a considerable contribution to the maintenance sector of the construction industry. Since maintenance of the Gross Capital Stock of Buildings relies upon such a broad contribution of input, a wide range of building activity is demanded. Such building work may be procured by large clients or public

1

bodies and undertaken by major building contractors operating at national level, or conversely, may be initiated by regionally or locally based clients and carried out by smaller building contractors. Clients may choose to undertake the work in-house using direct labour, if their organisation enables this, or work may be let openly or selectively through a tendered contract. Arrangements may adopt a formal structure and management approach or may be conducted on, what might be described as an *ad hoc* basis. Some building work will also be carried out by householders themselves using ostensibly DIY methods. The approach to maintaining and replenishing the Gross Capital Stock of Buildings and Works will, indeed, have considerable diversity but each contribution, however small, has a vital role to play.

A considerable proportion of construction output across the major sectors of repair and maintenance, rehabilitation, new build and housing, is undertaken within the category of *'small building works'*. This is a sphere of building construction that, whilst demonstrating many of the facets of all building work, also displays its own quite unique characteristics of organisation and management and experiences problems particular to its own area of activity. Although small building works tend to be thought of as, and are often subsumed within, other categories of construction activity, since they make such a considerable contribution to construction output they merit recognition in their own right.

Small building works can be extremely diverse in nature and range from what might be described as a minor building repair or maintenance task by a jobbing builder, to a new build project such as a major extension or even a complete building or structure. The various specific characteristics and criteria that define and differentiate the various types, size and value of such works are described in subsequent chapters. In order to appreciate the general nature, magnitude and importance of small building works within the building industry and its economy, it is necessary to review small building works in the context of construction output and the prevailing trends within the building and construction industry.

Construction output

Total construction output, in terms of statistical analysis, comprises the following elements:

(i) *New building work* – official statistics for new work output includes an element of extensions, alterations, site preparations and demolition in addition to all new build activity. Where extensions and alterations are applicable to housing, their output is included in the repair and maintenance category.

(ii) *Repair and Maintenance (Public Sector)* – includes repair and maintenance to all works except housing. It also includes an element of civil engineering activity which in general, receives less repair and maintenance expenditure than buildings.

(iii) *Repair and Maintenance (Private Sector)* – includes repair and maintenance to works other than housing. It excludes direct labour which is categorised separately.

(iv) *Housing Repair and Maintenance* – includes all work to existing dwellings, alterations and improvements.

(v) *Private Sector Directly Employed Labour (DEL)* – includes all works but usually excludes housing.

(vi) *Public Sector Directly Employed Labour (DEL)* – includes all works but usually excludes housing.

(vii) *Householder's Expenditure on DIY materials* – includes materials purchased by householders/occupiers for use in repair and maintenance of dwellings. An indeterminate proportion will be purchased by jobbing builders/trades for use in domestic dwelling work.

It is difficult to derive precise figures and distributions for particular elements of demand such as small building works from the overall construction industry output figures. Estimated statistics such as those determined by the Government Statistical Service and Building Maintenance Information compile their figures from a variety of sources and estimate to present overall trends in construction output. When interpretating such data, they must be treated carefully and with caution.

Total construction output

Statistics[1] show that total construction output in 1989/90 was in excess of £42 billion per annum. Total output has risen steadily from £19 billion in 1980 to the 1989/90 level. Rate of growth has been accelerating, with the exception of a short-term fall in output in 1981. Since then, it has risen at the average rate of £3 billion per annum. The general distribution of total construction output is 59 per cent new building work and 41 per cent repair and maintenance activity. Of the total output in repair and maintenance, 22 per cent is devoted to housing while 10 per cent and 9 per cent is apportioned to public sector (non-housing) and private sector (non-housing) repair and maintenance respectively. This distribution is shown in Figure 1.1.

Small building works will assume only a minor proportion of activity in the new build sector and, in the main, will be concerned with extensions, alterations or improvement works. The greatest proportion of small building works is likely to occur in the repair and maintenance sector.

Total Construction Output £46.2 billion p.a.
Repair and Maintenance (41 per cent) £18.9 billion p.a.

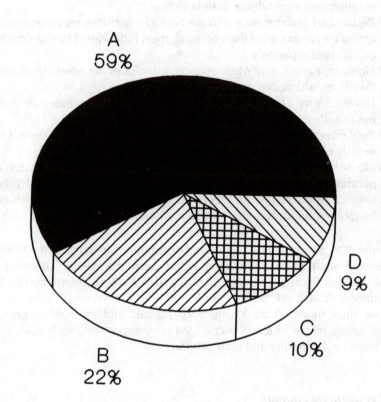

A: New Building Work   £27.3 billion
B: Housing, Repair and Maintenance   £10.3 billion
C: Public Sector, Repair and Maintenance   £4.6 billion
D: Private Sector, Repair and Maintenance   £4.0 billion
  (i)   All figures based on current prices.
 (ii)   Figures rounded up for ease of presentation.
(iii)   New build work includes civil engineering.
 (iv)   Figures for new build work include elements for extensions, major
        alterations (improvements).
  (v)   Housing extensions, major allocations (improvements) and con-
        versions are included in repairs and maintenance.
 (vi)   Figures exclude maintenance work in the private sector carried out by
        direct labour.

Figure 1.1 Distribution of UK construction output

Repair and maintenance output

Figure 1.2 illustrates the distribution of total maintenance expenditure and includes two categories of construction output not reflected in Figure 1.1, these being Private Sector (non-housing) Direct Labour and DIY Building Materials. Housing repair and maintenance assumes the largest proportion of construction output in this sector, some 39 per cent, whilst 17 per cent is expended in public sector (non housing) and 15 per cent in private sector (non-housing). Private sector (non-housing) Directly Employed Labour (DEL) accounts for 10 per cent of repair and maintenance output. The second

Total Output £26.3 billion p.a.

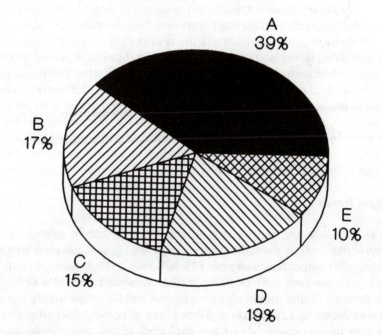

A: Housing, Repair and Maintenance
B: Public Sector, Repair and Maintenance
C: Private Sector, Repair and Maintenance
D: DIY, expenditure on materials
E: Private Sector (non-housing) Direct Labour
  (i) All figures based on current prices.
  (ii) Figures rounded up for ease of presentation.
  (iii) Repair and maintenance output includes housing, Public and Private Sector repair and maintenance (see Figure 1.1).

Figure 1.2 Distribution of total maintenance expenditure

largest proportion of total repair and maintenance output is that expenditure by householders or occupiers on DIY materials for housing upkeep, this being some 19 per cent or, in monetary terms, nearly £5 billion per annum. DIY is excluded from any estimates since it does not contribute directly to any construction sector. The majority of small building works are likely to occur within the sector of repair and maintenance and in all sub-sectors, although more so in some than others.

Construction output by direct labour

Total construction output excludes maintenance and repair carried out in the private sector by direct labour. There are no statistics available for this sector. Figures do, however, estimate the output of direct labour based upon the relationship between contract work and directly employed labour in the private sector. Figure 1.3 illustrates the distribution of maintenance output between direct labour and contracted work. The distribution varies according to construction sector, for example in general building the distribution is 30 per cent and 70 per cent for direct labour and contract labour respectively, whilst in the services sector the distribution would be nearer a 50 per cent – 50 per cent apportionment. Combined figures for all construction work is estimated by Building Maintenance Information[1] to be 38 per cent directly employed labour and 62 per cent contracted. Figure 1.3 shows the distribution for building maintenance only.

Output trends

Figure 1.4 illustrates the repair and maintenance output relative to total construction output over the period 1979–89. It will be seen that total construction output has risen from £19 billion in 1979 to over £46 billion in 1989, with the only setback being a slight downturn in 1981. Repair and maintenance output including direct labour and DIY expenditure has risen to be in excess of £26 billion or 59 per cent of construction output. If DIY and directly employed labour are excluded, repair and maintenance in housing amounts to some £18.9 billion or 41 per cent of total industry output. This sector is continuing to rise in monetary terms, although repair and maintenance as a percentage of total construction output rose from 38 per cent in 1979, peaked in 1985 at 46.4 per cent and decreased to 41 per cent in 1989.

Estimates presented in the report 'Building Britain 2001'[2] suggests that repair and maintenance is anticipated to rise by over 34 per cent in the period 1989 to 2001, whilst growth in the new build sector is likely to rise by less than 15 per cent. These figures, however, take no account of activity in the first few years of the 1990s where, after reaching a peak in 1989, construction output was estimated by the National Economic Development

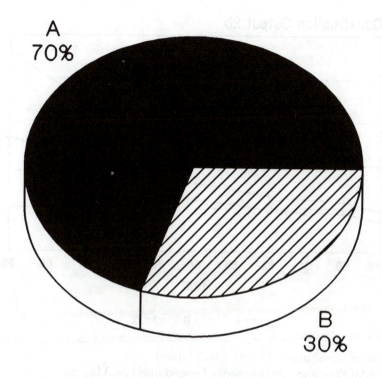

A: Contracted repair and maintenance
B: Direct labour repair and maintenance
  (i) All figures based on current prices.
  (ii) Figures rounded up for ease of presentation.
  (iii) Figures are for building maintenance output.
  (iv) Variations in distribution occur in different construction sectors.

Figure 1.3 Distribution of building maintenance output to direct labour and contracted works

Office (NEDO)[3] to be on a severe downturn due to the sharp decline in commercial work and continued difficulties in funding availability.

The implication for small building works is, of course, that as repair and maintenance assumes a higher proportion of the available construction activity so the propensity for jobbing works, small works and minor building projects increases. There will be greater emphasis towards repairing, modifying and up-grading existing buildings and a move away from new build construction projects.

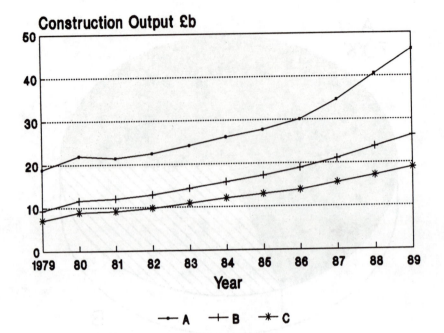

Construction Output £b

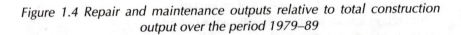

A: Total Construction Output £46.2 billion
B: Total Repair and Maintenance Expenditure £26.3 billion
    (including DIY, Direct Labour outputs)
C: Repair and maintenance output (housing, other
    public and private sector output) £18.9 billion

Figure 1.4 Repair and maintenance outputs relative to total construction output over the period 1979–89

1.2 Economic significance of small building works

Figure 1.5 shows the estimated value of small building works output in relation to total output in each construction sector. Small building works account for approximately £9 billion of annual construction demand or almost one-fifth of total annual construction output. Its economic significance is, therefore, clearly evident. Calculating the definitive output of small building works is however, far from easy. It relies for its estimation not just upon known figures for small works output but upon activities and trends in other sectors. There are no readily available statistics isolating this construction activity from which figures can simply be extracted.

Small building works output occurs in three pertinent areas, each of which is defined and described in Chapter 2, these are;

Elements of Construction Output

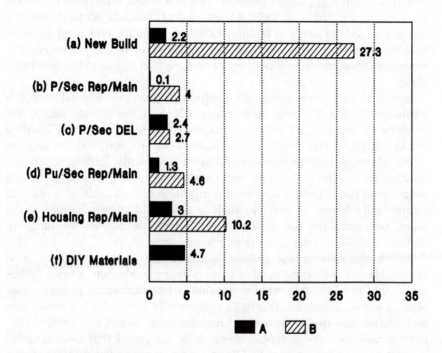

A: Value of small building works.
B: Value of construction output.
  (i) DIY materials are excluded from small works calculations, although
       shown in the above figure for reference purposes.

*Figure 1.5 Estimated value of small building works output in relation to total
output in each construction sector*

  (i) *Jobbing works*
 (ii) *Ordered works*
(iii) *Small/minor building projects*

It is the combination of activity in these three areas that comprises small
building works output. Explaining the basis of these figures is, therefore,
important.

Just over £2.2 billion (8 per cent) is spent on small building works in the
sector of new build. Building Maintenance Information statistics[1] show that
new build accounts for over £27 billion, with extensions, alterations and
improvements, to buildings other than housing included in the total, many

of which are being contracted on a small building works basis. To verify this estimate, statistics published by the Royal Institution of Chartered Surveyors (RICS)[4] show that in a survey of forms of contract used, taken from nearly ten per cent of new orders in 1989, 41 per cent of contracts adopted were the recognised shorter forms of building contract, being the type used for small building works. In proportion to the construction output surveyed, this represents approximately 8 per cent of construction output in the new build sector.

Statistics[1] show that almost £2.7 billion (6 per cent) of total output is attributed to directly employed labour (DEL) in the private sector, the majority of which, £2.4 billion, is suggested to be in the small building works category. The majority of private sector organisations employing direct labour will utilize their expenditure in, primarily, jobbing repair and maintenance to the built assets, and undertake this on both a planned and un-planned basis. Only a very small proportion of their activity is likely to be directed towards other works such as new build as these would, in the main, be contracted out as their requirements lie outside the range of abilities and skills of the direct labour force.

Within the category of private sector repair and maintenance it is impossible to make an estimate of small building works output since figures are simply not available. Whilst housing is homogeneous, private sector repair and maintenance comprises a vast array of assets. A small proportion will require day-to-day repair and maintenance, whilst the greatest pro-portion will be capital replacement. It is suggested that only a small proportion, £0.1 billion from £4 billion output, is expended in this area, this figure being derived from the relationship between private sector (non-housing) maintenance expenditure against capital stock which indicates that approximately only 1.6 per cent is expended annually.

The output from small building works in public sector repair and main-tenance and housing repair and maintenance are the most arguable figures to be derived from total construction output. Figures[1] show that housing repair and maintenance and public sector repair and maintenance account for 22 per cent and 10 per cent of total output respectively. Based on the general distribution of planned and un-planned repair and maintenance in the private sector, in both housing and non-housing fields, 70 per cent of work would be planned or scheduled repair and maintenance undertaken by direct labour and the remaining 30 per cent un-planned works usually carried out on a contract basis by small building firms. Using this 30 per cent total as a notional benchmark, expenditure on small building works equates to £1.3 billion and £3 billion in public sector repair and maintenance and housing repair and maintenance respectively.

Based upon the estimated total small building works output of £9 billion (or 19 per cent) of total construction output, the distribution of small works activity in each sector is represented in Figure 1.6. This distribution represents overall activity in jobbing works, ordered works and small/minor building projects. It is simply not possible to categorise each individually since accurate statistics are not available. As a percentage of total construction output, small building works currently account for approximately one-fifth, a considerably large figure in its own right and therefore, the significance of these works within construction industry is clear to see. This is likely to be further emphasised as repair and maintenance rises as a proportion of total construction output, since as it rises so too does the propensity for small building works to increase in parallel. One might therefore, expect to see small building works accounting for a quarter or more of all construction output by the turn of the century.

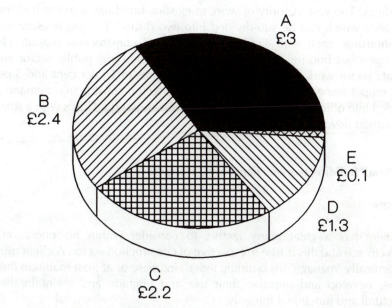

A: Housing, repair and maintenance.
B: Private Sector direct labour.
C: New build.
D: Public Sector, repair and maintenance.
E: Private Sector, repair and maintenance.
  (i) all figures based on current prices.
  (ii) figures rounded up for ease of presentation.
  (iii)distribution of planned and un-planned repair and maintenance based
       on 70 per cent/30 per cent.
  iv DIY is excluded from all calculations.

Figure 1.6 Distribution of small building works output

1.3 Distribution of demand

Figure 1.7 illustrates the distribution of demand within the construction industry. The figures presented are approximate, based on the published statistics for total construction output. They should, therefore, be appreciated for general guidance only. New build work currently accounts for some 59 per cent of total construction output, although it should be remembered that an element within this total represents extensions and major alterations and improvements to existing buildings. Output said to be wholly involved with existing buildings is 41 per cent. A small percentage is devoted to civil engineering, although it should be remembered that civil engineering work always has a lower level of maintenance expenditure than buildings. The vast majority of work to existing buildings is in the building category, which can be sub-divided into two distinct groups, housing and non-housing, each with similar proportions of construction output. The homogeneous housing sector is, again, sub-divided into public sector and private sector work, with disproportionate figures of 18 per cent and 3 per cent output respectively. In the non-housing sector, construction demand is divided into offices and other facilities on an almost equal basis with a small proportion devoted to shop buildings.

1.4 Small building works: clients and contractors

Clients

A client has a great many factors to consider within his operational marketplace and this is true irrespective of construction sector. A client must dynamically 'manage' his building assets, increase or at least maintain their value, develop and improve their use and upgrade and maintain their structural and functional integrity.

As the construction output for small building works is currently reflected in a figure of approximately one-fifth of total construction activity and future demand looks set to rise rather than diminish, the increasing significance of small building works should be reflected in the level of importance demonstrated by clients. Certainly, if statistics for the future[2] come to fruition, the growing demand for repair and maintenance is likely to increase the propensity for small building works growth largely in parallel. Small works growth will not just be seen in the repair and maintenance sector however. If there is a tailing-off in demand for major building projects then there will be some sector-based shift towards smaller building projects, where again, the attributes of small building works may be exploited. In overall terms therefore, clients are unlikely to regard small building works in the future as anything other than a serious building activity.

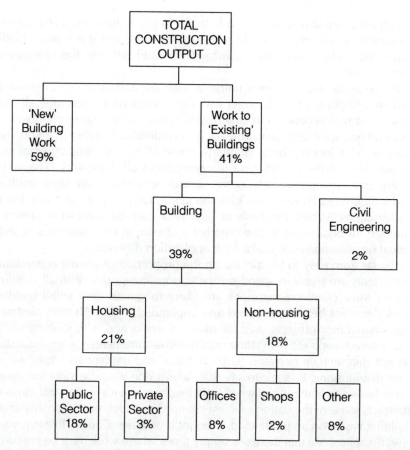

Figure 1.7 Distribution of demand within the construction industry

Client bodies are many and varied and function within many market sectors. Small building works undertaken by any client and in any sector may fall into one of the three categories identified previously, namely: jobbing works; ordered works; and small/minor building projects. The way in which a client will view small building work categories will vary according to circumstances. In general, one can separate the various forms of approach into those works which are planned construction activities and those which are un-planned. Planned building works require a considerable amount of forethought and tend, in the main, to be more major projects which are likely to be procured using one of the shorter standard forms of building contract. This will therefore, be viewed by the client as small/minor building projects. Works which are, for any reason, un-planned, generally fall into the category of jobbing works or ordered works. The fundamental difference between these two latter groups is in the way in which the client structures the work, that is to say, if the work is arranged on an almost casual basis it would be a jobbing work and if it is more highly structured and professionally managed it would fall into the category of ordered works.

Whilst some major clients utilise a planned and structured approach, perhaps adopting a term contract with one contractor to look after all their repair and maintenance and small build requirements, other clients use a more *ad hoc* approach, procuring each job individually either as an ordered work or on a jobbing basis. Similarly, some clients use directly employed labour whilst other clients have to contract out all their work. The philosophy and concepts underlying the various approaches are very involved and will, obviously, vary from client to client. Certainly, no one role fits all organisations. Whilst the basis of approach may be somewhat common amongst all organisations, the different and unique characteristics of individual organisations will make each application different.

It is far from easy to be specific on the proportion of annual expenditure that clients are likely to spend on the various categories of small building works. Most client organisations are likely to spread their small building work demands between planned and unplanned work with term contracts and small/minor projects used for planned works and with jobbing works and ordered works satisfying their unplanned requirements. General statistics do not differentiate between term contracts and unplanned works within their distributions. It is fair to say that, whilst one would expect the major client bodies to lean toward wholly planned works with recognised forms of contract, some of the nation's largest clients do, in fact, procure many small building works on an unplanned, even jobbing basis. Clients, like everyone else, do appreciate that there are simply times where work must be procured on an *ad hoc* jobbing basis simply to get the job done quickly, but it is also well recognised that there are pitfalls and disadvantages in adopting such an approach. These pitfalls and problems for the client are reviewed extensively in subsequent chapters.

Clients are, of course, also influenced by factors outside their control when contemplating small works management. Significant influences are:

- Current commercial considerations
- Legislation
- Conservation and environmental issues.

In commercial sectors particularly, markets change rapidly due to user or customer trends. New working methods, innovation and even consumer fashions may dictate the need for property up-grade, alterations and extensions. A client cannot ignore these factors. Similarly, legislation must be recognised and the range of planning and building control acts will impart great influence upon how the client manages building assets. Many buildings may well be properties listed as being of historical importance and this too will influence quite significantly how a client seeks to undertake small works to such buildings.

Contractors

Small building works open up a large annual construction market for building contractors, both large and small. In fact, in simple terms, the greatest proportion of general employment within the construction industry is within small building firms, those that rely heavily upon small building works for their survival.

In general, it may said that there is never quite enough construction work to go around and indeed this is true of the small building works market. Even in a vast multi-million pound industry any restriction squeezes the market considerably. Larger contractors diversify and come in to bid for medium size projects, medium size firms chase smaller projects and in extreme cases the small builders may be pushed out of the market completely. Such a situation means that those smaller and medium size builders who rely upon small works activity must be organised and very specialist in what they do.

Small building works are undertaken by small contractors operating within both general and specific fields of activity and amongst major contracting organisations who have specialist small works departments or divisions within their broader organisational frameworks. The vast majority of these contractors conduct small building works in a highly structured and professional way, leading to, in the main, complete success and customer satisfaction. Unfortunately, *ad hoc* jobbing works, with which all small building works are easily confused, are not undertaken quite as effectively or expeditiously as one would like, leading to considerable customer dissatisfaction. It is this minor element of construction activity which rubs off on the construction industry generally, and more specifically, harms small building works, since inefficiency and shoddy workmanship are often the basis upon which public perception of construction is founded.

The construction industry has, for years, been aware of and concerned with the poor image of building construction in the eyes of the public and appreciates all too well those undesirable activities of the small minority of jobbing builders who do let the industry down so badly. Various initiatives within industry, such as BS 5750: quality assurance schemes and independent third party certification has attempted to alleviate such problems but it is a slow process and, indeed, such initiatives rarely contribute at the smaller firm end of the industry in any case. The general public almost exclusively forms its opinion based upon their dealings with jobbing builders, since the vast majority of work for the public will be procured from these sources rather than from major building contractors. Where things go wrong, as they will from time to time, the lack of formal structure, contract and legal redress only leads the customer to complete dissatisfaction, not only with the individual builder but it also leaves a bitter taste in the mouth and scant respect for the building industry as a whole.

Within the building industry itself there are mixed feelings about small building works. Many contractors, in particular the larger ones, feel they do not wish to take on small works for fear of being branded as a jobbing or 'cowboy' builder. Some contractors do not even like to be referred to as 'general' building contractors for the same reason. As the building industry changes its profile, as indeed it must with economic circumstance, when there is less new build and fewer major building projects so small building works come into their own. At times, contractors have to respect small building works as the staple diet of their work load, supplemented with new build work as and when it is available. Indeed, many larger contractors undertake small works for major clients on a term contract basis and find that this provides their regular and stable turnover and income whilst risking the tendering process in other areas of activity. Small works may not afford the most lucrative profit margins but the work is continuous and steady and, therefore, becomes an anchor during hard economic times.

Certainly, the general presentation of public and private sector building stock is essential to the nation's long-term well-being and this relies heavily upon small works to sustain its existence and for continued improvement. This is the macro level. On the micro level, the building industry is judged on the condition and presentation of the nation's buildings and it is at this level where the public forms its impressions and opinions of: the construction industry generally; of the way work is undertaken; and of the organisations, both large and small who operate within it. It must be clearly demonstrated that the organisation and management of small works is a professional activity and one which is on a par with other more major building projects within the industry. Only in this way will small building works be perceived as the important activity it is and receive the due recognition, both within and outside the industry, it truly deserves.

References

1 Building Maintenance Information. *The Economic Significance of Maintenance,* (1991), BMI Special Report, serial 198, ISBN 0–90- 6182–56–5
2 Centre for Strategic Studies in Construction, University of Reading, *Building Britain 2001,* (1988), ISBN 07049–0942–1
3 National Economic Development Office. (NEDO) *Construction Forecasts,* (1990–92), Joint Forecasting Committee, NEDO
4 Royal Institution of Chartered Surveyors, *Contracts in Use,* (1991), *Chartered Quantity Surveyor,* Jan 1991.

2 The Nature of Small Building Works

2.1 Characteristics

Compiling a precise and complete definition for small building works is far from straightforward. In the same way that the nature and characteristics of small building works are analogous, in part, with other building works but may also be considerably diverse, so too are the various perceptions and interpretations of small building works. General perception within the building industry recognises small works as new works, alterations, modifications, improvements and aspects of maintenance work of a 'general building nature' up to a cost value of approximately £70 000 (at 1989 prices). Confusion however, often surrounds what kind of activity constitutes a small building work. If a small work is by definition small, then what does 'small' actually represent, is it value, size, characteristics or technical complexity? To provide some measure of understanding it is essential to identify and differentiate between the various types of building activity that broadly constitutes small building works.

Small building works can be said to include all building activities that fall into the three groups of:

i   *Jobbing works*
ii   *Ordered works*
iii *Small/minor building projects*

Small building works, in general, may be said to display a number of discernible characteristics which distinguish them from other building works, these are:

- *They have limited scale* – may be measured in terms of cost value, although different ranges of value may be denoted by cost bands, each with an upper cost limit, for example small building works up to £1000, £2500, £5000, (limits may be lower or higher depending upon circumstances).
- *They have limited content* – usually, though not exclusively, small building works have low technical complexity although, nevertheless, they are often highly labour intensive and may require the input of most

17

building trades and skills and necessitate the usual operational sequence of production activities.

- *They have small quantities* – the building operations involved usually entail small quantities in terms of materials required and labour tasks performed. Again, there can be wide parameters since the quantities will be influenced by the cost involved and these vary with different cost bands and their upper cost limits.
- *They may be unspecified, of an uncertain nature or even be of an unknown nature prior to their commencement* – some small works cannot be defined, described or quantified prior to their undertaking.

  If measurement is not possible, they may be costed by their labour, plant and materials input, (*daywork rates*). Uncertainty usually dictates that the works are not well specified and there is minimal control documentation.
- *They have a short production duration* – most small building works, though not all, will be completed within a short duration, i.e. within one to three months from their commencement.

Two further characteristics of small building works are deliberately separated from the aforementioned. Particular attention is drawn to these characteristics and the discussions that follow later in this chapter.

- *They may be 'jobbing' works* – some small building works may be procured without reference to formal contracts, may be negotiated verbally (spot pricing) without the provision of written quotations and may be undertaken by unskilled or semi-skilled building operatives.
- *They may be more advanced building works* – some building works will be of greater size, value and complexity than jobbing works and ordered works and therefore will come into the classification of 'small/ minor building projects'. Such building works are characterised, and their operational parameters determined, by the form of agreement or contract made between the client and contractor. (It is from this that the upper cost value parameter, £70 000, is generally recognised.)

Small building works have characteristics in addition to the aforementioned, some of which they share with other building and construction works. Such works may be:

- Greatly diverse in nature.
- Require general building skills or specialised inputs.
- Piecemeal in content and approach.
- Likely to be undertaken simultaneously with other small building works.
- Of different priority levels, i.e. emergency, urgent or routine works.
- Carried out by one building contractor who undertakes all the works involved.

In general, the two main characteristics that differentiate jobbing works, ordered works and small/minor building projects are, the cost value of the work which determines the second characteristic, the degree of formality between the client/customer and the builder/craft operative. Typically, the greater the value of the work to be undertaken, the greater the degree of formality and more clearly defined the relationship between the parties, although there are other factors which bear influence upon the arrangement. See Figure 2.1.

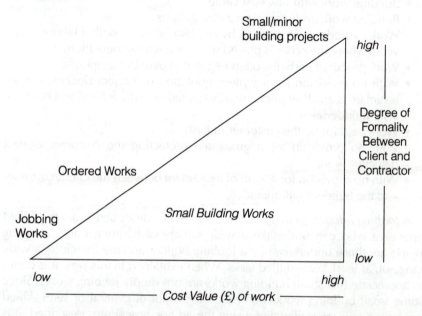

Figure 2.1 Relationship between cost value and degree of formality in small building works

2.2 Jobbing works

Jobbing works may be defined as:

> *those works carried out to instruction, but without prior written quotation, without documentation and without a formal arrangement between the client/employer and builder/craft operative.*

Due to their typical nature and characteristics, small building works are frequently regarded simply as little more than jobbing works. This is unfortunate, since the term jobbing works as defined is generally work carried out on a casual basis by unskilled or semi-skilled labour, is conducted without written documentation and which is often paid for cash-in-hand. Whilst indeed, many small works are carried out on such a basis, this paints a somewhat derisory picture of small building works which is far from the real nature of small building works organisation and management. It is, in general, the image of the 'cowboy' builder which is conjured up in the eyes of the public and this inaccurate perception is, in the main, both unnecessary and undesirable.

Jobbing work is frequently associated with:

- Building work with low cost value.
- Building work undertaken on a casual basis.
- Work carried out, in general, by unskilled or semi-skilled labour.
- Work where the order is placed without a written quotation.
- Work procured verbally, often negotiated over the telephone.
- With no provision for a written quotation or project documentation, (estimate is an all-in price, usually quoted verbally following a brief site visit, if undertaken).
- Work paid for by the customer in cash.
- With no provision for a guarantee protecting the customer against defective work.
- With no provision for a form of agreement between the client/customer and the builder/craft operative.

A *Jobbing builder*, (craft operative), is generally described as a semi-skilled operative who can undertake a wide variety of building trades. *Jobbing works* are those undertaken by a jobbing builder and are therefore, a wide range of, at least, semi-skilled tasks. When explained in this way, it is easier to appreciate that small building works are not simply jobbing works. Since some small building works do require the input of general or semi-skilled operatives and are undertaken using the *ad hoc* procedures described, it is also easy to see how confusion arises.

Individual small building works, procured using a written order are, in fact, the subject of a structured and well recognised procurement approach, yet are sometimes inappropriately referred to as jobbing works. Rarely, if indeed ever, are jobbing works procured using a written contract between the client and contractor. Quotations, if provided, do sometimes present conditions on the reverse side of the quote which loosely represents the basis upon which the builder is prepared to carry out the work. The level of definition, description and information is nowhere near as precise nor as thorough as the information presented in a client's request for quotation or a written (works) order. More often than not, the whole undertaking is a verbal understanding between the customer and the builder/craft operative.

Jobbing works do, of course, have their place within the industry. For example, a homeowner requiring a minor building/plumbing task such as the installation of an outside cold water tap, is hardly going to obtain a number of quotations from different companies, but will simply engage a locally-based and suitable craft operative (tradesman) to acquire a quotation, usually verbal, and pay for the work in cash when completed. It would be uneconomic to procure the work in any other way.

While jobbing works, in a true sense, are undertaken as described, a recently introduced 'Standard Form of Contract for Building Work of a Jobbing Character', under the Joint Contracts Tribunal (JCT) seeks to give jobbing works a more positive and structured approach. This form of contract is described in Chapter 5.

2.3 Ordered works

Ordered works may be defined as:

> *those works which are too large to adopt a jobbing works approach yet are insufficiently large to justify the use of a standard shorter form of building contract, but are works which require a structured approach to procurement and management and utilise documentation and a formal written agreement between the client and builder.*

The largest proportion of small building works will fall into the category of ordered works. (See Figure 2.2.) Such works are characterised by the following attributes:

- They may be procured from a small general or specialist building contractor or from a small building works department or division of a large building contracting organisation.
- They are procured after a request for quotation has been issued and a written quotation received.
- They are procured in a formalised way using official written orders such as a Works Order, (*a client's authorisation for work*).
- They are carried out under a written agreement between the client and contractor. (Form of agreement likely to be client's own and not a standard agreement).
- They are undertaken on an individual basis, procured by a works or daywork order.
- Alternative to above, they are carried out as part of an annual or term contract. (Form of agreement will be more comprehensive in this case.)
- Used where an element of competition (*tendering*) in procurement is preferred, but which may often be precluded by the nature and scale of the work.
- Are undertaken with reference to control documentation, i.e. drawings, specifications, schedules, etc.
- Involve formal and structured organisation and management procedures that may be similar to those used for other building work

generally, although their specialist nature have particular additional requirements.

- Have a limited cost value: within a range up to say £5000, although most works will typically be within smaller cost ranges, say £1000 or £2500.

Single contractor

The nature of ordered works, whether they be concerned with general or specialist building, are usually carried out by a single contractor and therefore, sub-contracts do not generally feature in their organisation. There may be occasions where the work necessitates the input of more than one contractor, where for example a proportion of the work is general building and a proportion specialist works. In such a case, the client will usually procure the two contractors using individual contracts with both contractors being responsible to the client and instructed by the client's works super-intendent. There may be situations where the client requests the contractor to procure the sub-contractor on the client's behalf. This may arise where, for example, the vast majority of the work is general building to be undertaken by the main contractor and a small part of the works being of a specialist nature for which the contractor has to rely upon the expertise of another. In such a case, the contractor will assume responsibility for the sub-contractor following normal contractual procedures.

2.4 Small/minor building projects

Small/minor building projects may be defined as:

those building works procured under a standard shorter form of building contract.

It is easy to confuse small/minor building projects in the context described with other building work carried out under particular standard forms of building contract. The use of the Faculty of Architects and Surveyors Small Works Contract[1] for example, is denoted as a 'small works' contract yet is:

intended for use with smaller building work (such as private houses or alterations or extensions) described by drawings and/or specifications or a schedule of work.

Such a form of contract, as identified from its definition and description, is designed for use on more complex or higher value projects, but without reference to the specific criteria characterising the various small building works confusion is likely. Similar ambiguity exists in the term 'minor works' as used in a variety of building contracts.[2,3,4,5] These contracts are defined,

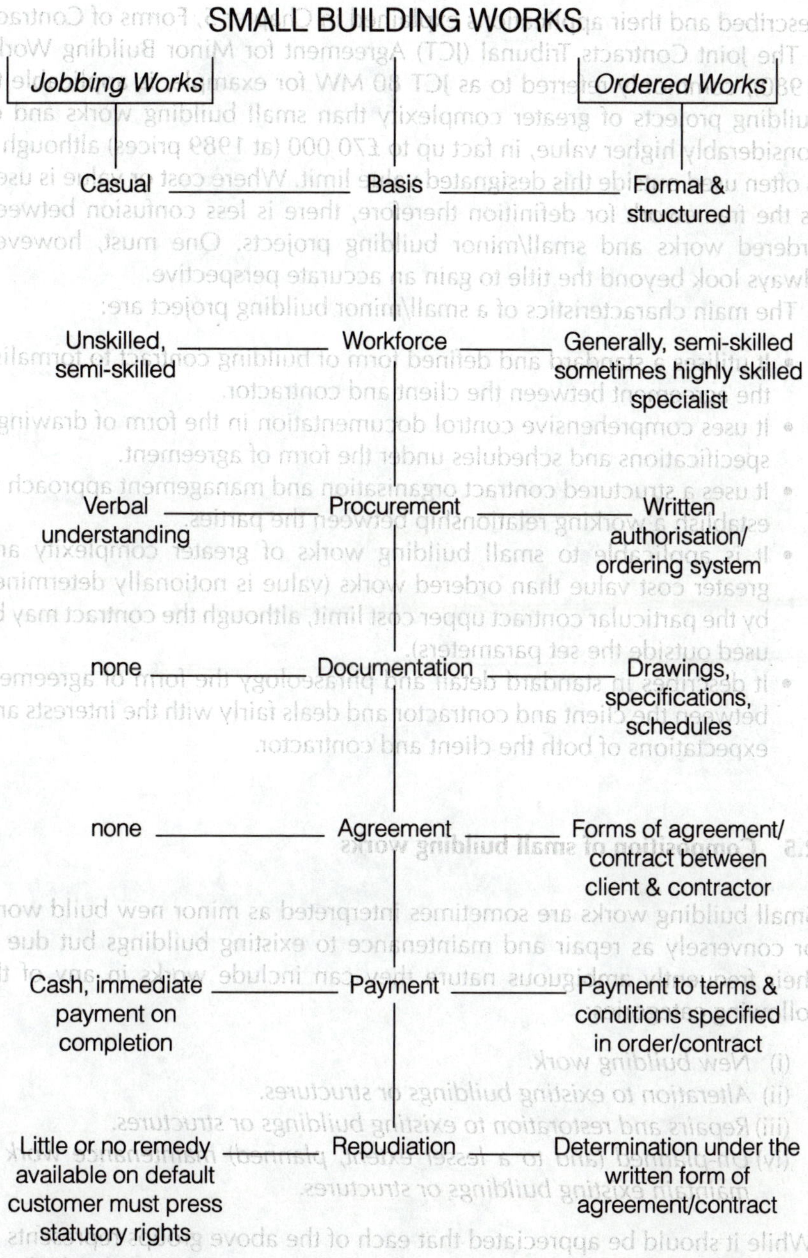

SMALL BUILDING WORKS

Jobbing Works		*Ordered Works*
Casual	Basis	Formal & structured
Unskilled, semi-skilled	Workforce	Generally, semi-skilled sometimes highly skilled specialist
Verbal understanding	Procurement	Written authorisation/ ordering system
none	Documentation	Drawings, specifications, schedules
none	Agreement	Forms of agreement/ contract between client & contractor
Cash, immediate payment on completion	Payment	Payment to terms & conditions specified in order/contract
Little or no remedy available on default customer must press statutory rights	Repudiation	Determination under the written form of agreement/contract

Figure 2.2 Differentiation between jobbing works and ordered works

described and their applications explained in Chapter 5, Forms of Contract.

The Joint Contracts Tribunal (JCT) Agreement for Minor Building Works (1980), commonly referred to as JCT 80 MW for example, is applicable to building projects of greater complexity than small building works and of considerably higher value, in fact up to £70 000 (at 1989 prices) although it is often used outside this designated value limit. Where cost or value is used as the framework for definition therefore, there is less confusion between ordered works and small/minor building projects. One must, however, always look beyond the title to gain an accurate perspective.

The main characteristics of a small/minor building project are:

- It utilises a standard and defined form of building contract to formalise the agreement between the client and contractor.
- It uses comprehensive control documentation in the form of drawings, specifications and schedules under the form of agreement.
- It uses a structured contract organisation and management approach to establish a working relationship between the parties.
- It is applicable to small building works of greater complexity and greater cost value than ordered works (value is notionally determined by the particular contract upper cost limit, although the contract may be used outside the set parameters).
- It describes in standard detail and phraseology the form of agreement between the client and contractor and deals fairly with the interests and expectations of both the client and contractor.

2.5 Composition of small building works

Small building works are sometimes interpreted as minor new build works or conversely as repair and maintenance to existing buildings but due to their frequently ambiguous nature they can include works in any of the following categories:

(i) *New building work.*
(ii) *Alteration to existing buildings or structures.*
(iii) *Repairs and restoration to existing buildings or structures.*
(iv) *Un-planned (and to a lesser extent, planned) maintenance work to maintain existing buildings or structures.*

While it should be appreciated that each of the above groups represents an area of building activity in its own right, some clients, in particular the larger ones procuring multiple small works under an annual or term contract, will expect contractors to undertake small works within any of these categories within the one contract, and not differentiate between the works. In reality, it is often difficult to distinguish between alterations, repairs, modernisation or maintenance work onsite and the differences may not really matter to the client as long as the work is done, although each can be defined and described individually. It is pertinent to say that while many of the aspects involved in the above are common, there are also distinguishing characteristics which necessitate some differences in concept and approach to their organisation and management.

The following description will aid to clarify the various types or categories of small building works (see Figure 2.3).

- *New building works* – may be subdivided into two categories:

  (i) (a) *Erection of new building or structure.*
  (b) *Replacement* – of an existing building or structure on the same site where the original building has been demolished.
  (ii) *Alterations* – new building work added to an existing building (extensions).

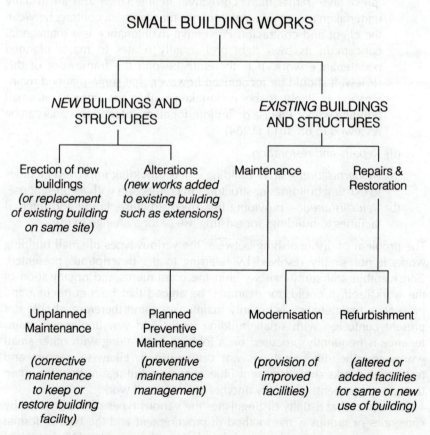

Figure 2.3 Variations in types of small building works

- *Existing building works* – may be categorised into two main groups, each of which can be subdivided and described as follows:

  (i) *Maintenance:*

     (a) *Unplanned repair and maintenance* – necessary to maintain or restore the integrity of the building or structure, or parts of it; also termed 'corrective' maintenance. These works are often procured in the same way as small new build works because of the intrinsic operations and approach displaying similar characteristics. They may be carried out under term contracts along with other small building works.

     (b) *Preventive maintenance* – sometimes referred to as planned preventive maintenance (PPM). Such works, while fulfilling the same basic requirements as unplanned maintenance, i.e. to maintain the integrity of buildings or structures or, parts of it, generally refer to 'preventive' rather than 'corrective' maintenance and are usually undertaken as part of a maintenance management contract between the client and contractor. Preventive maintenance is a managerial concept in its own right and usually relates to major planned maintenance work. It is therefore beyond the framework of this review. It should be recognised however, that some planned maintenance is likely to be undertaken within the context of small building works. Precise definitions for all maintenance works can be reviewed in BS 3811 (1984).

  (ii) *Repairs and restoration*

     (a) *Modernisation* – small building works providing improved facilities to existing buildings or structures in connection with its present use.

     (b) *Refurbishment* – providing improved structure, fabric and internal facilities to buildings for existing use or for a change in use.

The problem of distinguishing between the various types of small building works is not simply resolved by referring to the descriptions presented. Considerable ambiguity exists within the constituents and organisation of the work itself. It could, for example, be argued that both corrective and preventive maintenance is broadly maintenance and therefore, should not present confusion with small building works and yet, unplanned maintenance is frequently procured on a jobbing basis along with other small works and the different types not distinguished. Likewise, repairs and restoration works should present little confusion but again, they are often thought of by clients as simply another type of small work.

The aspect that usually distinguishes the various types of small works by categories or groups is the method of procurement and the type of formal arrangement or contract between the client and contractor. Where any of the aforementioned activities are procured on a jobbing basis it is usual to loosely term them small works, whereas those procured under a particular form of agreement or contract are generally denoted by the title and definition of the contract, i.e. small works contract, minor works project, maintenance contract, and the like.

While it would be virtually impossible to provide an exhaustive list of small building works, the following gives some indication of typical types of works:

Domestic
- Building extensions such as porches, conservatories and additional rooms.
- New building work such as garages.
- Modernisation such as retrofitting to kitchens and bathrooms.
- Alterations to existing layout to provide additional room or change in use of space.
- Repair, maintenance or refurbishment work to maintain existing structure, for example re-tiling and felting of a pitched roof.
- General upkeep and maintenance to maintain a building's well-being, for example painting.
- Modifications to a dwelling for upgrading facilities, such as wiring additional electrical services, provision of outside water services, provision of additional roof insulation, upgrading windows and doors.

Industrial
- Extension to existing building to provide additional working space.
- New building works to provide, for example offices, factory and production facilities.
- Re-fitting existing factory and office buildings to provide upgraded facility.
- Alterations to existing factory layout to provide additional space.
- Modification and upgrading of major services, for example pipe runs, ducting and electrical conduits.
- Provision of new or alterations to existing structures for production facilities such as pipework stanchion bases, machine plinths and the like.
- Minor external works including drainage works, roadworks and minor hard landscape.
- Repair, maintenance and refurbishment to maintain the well-being of existing buildings or structures, for example replacing sheet roof coverings or repairing damaged machine plinths.

2.6 The DIY building sector

It was identified in Chapter 1 that an element of total construction output is accounted for by DIY labour supplied by householders. This was estimated to be approximately ten per cent of total construction output or nearly

£5 billion per year in 1989.[6] This figure is derived from the value of DIY material purchased by householders for building work on their own dwellings, such as extensions, alterations and improvements as discussed in Chapter 1. Since the work constitutes DIY, it is discounted from the evaluation of output presented since it does support work in any construction sector. It is recognised however, that an element of this expenditure will be consumed by small builders and trades in undertaking jobbing works and small building and related works on behalf of householders, since some small builders and trades will resource their work through DIY and semi-retail/trade outlets. Five billion pounds per annum is a considerable sum of money but perhaps more significant than the total itself is the rate of growth of the DIY building sector. This sector multiplied four-fold over the 1980s and continues to be a rapidly growing building related market.

References

1   Faculty of Architects and Surveyors, *Small Works Contract*, Institute of Registered Architects.
2   Joint Contracts Tribunal, *Agreement for Minor Building Works*, Royal Institution of British Architects.
3   Faculty of Architects and Surveyors, *Minor Works Contract*, Institute of Registered Architects.
4   Scottish Building Contracts Committee, *Form for Minor Building Works*, SBCC.
5   Property Services Agency, *General Conditions of Government Contract for Building and Civil Engineering Minor Works*, Directorate of Building and Quantity Surveying Services, PSA.
6   Building Maintenance Information, *The Economic Significance of Maintenance*, (1991), BMI Special Report, serial 198.

3 Relationship between Clients and Contractors

General

Before entering into any relationship with a contractor to undertake small building works, the client will be concerned with a great many issues which can be broadly categorised under three headings:

(i) *Direct labour or contractor* – the client may choose between employing his own in-house labour force or contracting the work to a building contractor.

(ii) *Contractor selection* – when contracting small building works, the client must choose a contractor appropriate to the work and prevailing circumstance.

(iii) *Assessment of risk* – where a client procures any building project and enters into a relationship with a contractor, there will always be a degree of risk which must be considered.

3.1 Client employment of direct labour or contractor

One of the most contentious issues in the procurement of small building works is whether the client should:

(i) directly employ the labour force as part of the client's own organisation, (direct labour, often referred to as Directly Employed Labour – DEL).

(ii) Contract the work out to a building contractor.

In many cases, the choice between direct labour or contracted labour will not arise in the context of small building works. Many smaller clients in the private sector will simply not have the necessary organisation or resources to warrant such consideration. Similarly, many clients only procure small building works with such infrequency that the question, again, simply never arises. These clients will arrange for their small building work requirements to be met by local building contractors who will be engaged on a one-off basis, or if a larger project is envisaged, will have the work managed by an architect or surveyor using one of the available small building works or minor building works standard form of building contract.

29

For major clients in the private sector holding large building estates, commercial properties or industrial complexes, or large governmental or independent public sector organisations, the many issues surrounding the employment of direct labour or letting the work to a private contractor is an extremely vexed issue demanding serious consideration. It is quite revealing that a large number of the UK's largest client bodies with a high and constant demand for small new building works, alterations, maintenance and repair, procure their requirements through contracts let selectively or competitively to private contractors. They do not contemplate employing direct labour as part of their own organisation despite the fact that it may often appear to be expeditious and economically advantageous for them to do so.

Within the public sector, local authority direct labour organisations (DLOs) have proliferated for many years. An alternative to contracted labour, DLOs are said to provide maximum convenience with minimum cost, efficiency coupled with close control and flexibility. Whilst DLOs may have adhered to particular political standpoints or economic circumstances over the years, public accountability has brought them into question also. The introduction of the Local Government Planning and Land (Amendment) Act, 1980, has aimed to provide greater flexibility, more accountability and higher financial control over public works. This has affected, quite severely, the state of virtual perfect competition that DLOs had hitherto enjoyed. In many cases local authorities have been prevented from using direct labour and thus much public sector building, refurbishment and new work is contracted out by competitive tender.

It is somewhat axiomatic that the 'frequency' and 'volume' of small works must be at a sufficient level to justify consideration for such an argument in the first place. This accepted, probably the two most important factors to consider, thereafter, are:

(i)   The client organisation (its nature and characteristics).
(ii) Cost.

The client organisation

Where a client seeks to employ direct labour to undertake small works, the client organisation must be:

- Sufficiently large to support the direct labour organisation and structure.
- Financially sound to support the cost of the direct labour organisation.
- Able to provide the necessary managerial capability to administer the direct labour approach.

If the client is sufficiently large to financially sustain the employment of the required small works direct labour force, then one might reasonably draw the conclusion that it must be more viable to employ one's own labour than contract an outside builder, yet this argument alone is not always sound. Where the client is knowledgable and experienced in the design and management of the small works it requires, then it will be a more realistic proposition. Moreover, where the client can draw upon resources and expertise from within its own organisation then the argument for direct labour holds greater conviction. A client may, for example, have in its employ a number of good all-round general or building handymen who, with a little additional and specialised training, could form the core of a small works direct labour force.

Clients with design sections in the organisation, in manufacturing for example, may turn a hand to designing uncomplicated small works, whilst an in-house project or production manager could consider the management of minor building projects. This may allow many of the organisation's small works to be effectively managed in-house and let by contract only those larger works which the in-house team could not realistically handle. The specialist nature of construction, however, even when dealing only with small building works, is perhaps the main reason why clients are more readily disposed to letting the work to contract than considering the alternative. When small building works are beyond the remit of a jobbing work item, for example where the project requires full planning and building approval and work is of a specialised nature, then this work is best left to the professional building contractor and again a client is unlikely to consider a direct labour approach.

A client may choose to categorise small works as follows:

- Unskilled and semi-skilled small jobbing works.
- Conventional skilled *'ordered'* small building and related works.
- Specialist skilled *'ordered'* small building and related works.
- Small/minor building projects.

Most clients will vary their approach toward small works management according to the category into which their building requirement falls.

Direct labour should only be considered by a client where the volume and continuity of work can be planned for and, to some extent, guaranteed. Once the client has gone to the effort and expense of setting-up a direct labour organisation it has to keep that organisation employed. For this reason direct labour is usually kept to an absolute minimum for regular works such as minor maintenance and repair and the occasional new small work task. In a poor economic climate when the organisation may not have sufficient capital to invest in new work, improvements and repairs, it would not be a financially viable proposition to retain direct labour for the occasional and disparate small work item. In this situation the work would be let out to contract as and when required. For this reason, small works are divided into two distinct groups, those small works which are:

- Regular (routine/response) works (day-to-day requirement).
- Infrequent works (occasional requirement).

Should a situation arise where there is sufficient volume of work to justify the case for a term contract, then there is an argument for direct labour against letting the contract out to a contractor on a fixed price basis. Again the client must consider if it has the necessary knowledge, expertise and resources to manage the work in-house with work of equivalent quality and at a cost more favourable than contracting out the work to a building contractor.

Cost

The cost of employing direct labour or a contractor is a crucial area for consideration. Whereas the specialist small works building contractor has the capability to reduce its organisational overheads through its specialism and the application of that specialism to obtain economies of scale, the client seeking to use direct labour has a costly activity to face. In addition to the direct cost of the in-house labour force itself, there will be, perhaps, incalculable indirect cost to the organisation in terms of the provision of support facilities, management and clerical staff.

Cost to the organisation can be considered in two categories:

- *Direct cost* – including: national insurance contributions; super-annuation; holiday pay; travelling time payments; incentive bonus schemes; overtime payments; and related items.
- *Indirect cost* – which may itself be sub-divided into two groups:

  (a) Salaries and wages costs – including management; clerical staff; supervisors; and production staff.
  (b) Support facilities – including accommodation and temporary facilities; temporary services; transportation; handling and storage of materials.

In addition to those items mentioned, there may be additional cost incurred with the renting of accommodation; capital tied up in material stores; and tools and plant holdings. Where small works are needed in work locations remote from the permanent office facility, there will be additional costs in providing a temporary site organisation at each workplace. The aforementioned only represent the main costs involved in employing a direct labour force, the list is not exhaustive but serves to illustrate that the likely costs will be very high. It is not unreasonable to suggest that the overall cost of employing direct labour, taking one project in isolation, can be up to one and one half times, or even twice, the cost of procuring the work through a building contractor. Obviously, the greater the volume of work undertaken, the greater the propensity for economies of scale, but the high cost can make direct labour financially prohibitive. This provides yet another reason why clients tend to adopt an approach towards contracted labour.

In an attempt to alleviate some of the overhead costs, many clients employ mobile small works units. A mobile work gang can prove to be extremely useful in meeting the specific problems of working in remote locations where excessive travelling costs would be ordinarily cost prohibitive. An effective example of mobile small works approach is seen in the after sales, maintenance and repair service offered by major housebuilders. As commercial housebuilders are contractually responsible for rectifying certain building problems in new houses in the early life of the building through housing warranty schemes, the housebuilder is assured of a regular throughput of small works, maintenance and repair. To meet this commitment, it is more economic and practical to employ a small group of mobile operatives than to maintain an office based team that must travel to and from each work situation. Such approach also provides an urgent response or emergency call out facility which many clients also have need for. Many clients in other fields of activity realise the potential of mobile small works units which can reduce substantially the organisational overheads in retaining a direct labour force at a central base and where to procure the services of an outside contractor for each call out would be very expensive or even totally impractical.

Convenience and practicality

The choice between the employment of direct labour or contracted labour depends fundamentally upon the client organisation, circumstances and the influence that the various requirements for small building works have upon the management thinking of the client and upon cost. The choice, however, should not be based on cost alone, although cost is undoubtedly a crucial factor in the decision making process. Moreover, choice should combine the appreciation of cost with that of expected quality and performance of the respective labour force and should also consider the level of convenience to the client in using either form of labour. The client must balance the ability to provide the labour resource with cost, level of expectation and practicability. If any of these variables cannot be effectively accommodated then it is likely that direct labour would fail to be a viable proposition and the work should be let out to contract.

Combining direct labour with contracted labour

In practice, some larger client bodies will adopt a policy of mixing direct labour for some small works and contracting out other work to specialists and also general contractors. The difficult decision is then, of course, the distribution of type and volume of work between the two forms of approach.

It would be normal practice for a client to, say, arrange minor maintenance and repair work to be undertaken by a small complement of direct labour but nearly always contract out works which are more substantial and complex, such as new building work and larger building alterations. These more demanding projects would be carried out under a standard form of building contract rather than the former jobbing approach.

There are clearly arguments to support the selection of both direct labour and contractor and the ultimate decision is only likely to be made in the long-term rather than the immediate or short-term as all relevant factors, changing market conditions and the general economic climate will have to be considered, since they all have considerable bearing on the outcome (see Figure 3.1). When choosing between the employment of a direct labour force or building contractor the client must consider the following factors, both in respect of their individual properties and in their inter-relationship with other factors:

- Type of work.
- Volume of work.
- Likely cost.
- Expected performance and quality.
- Client's capability to carry out the work.
- Convenience of approach.
- External commercial climate, markets and environmental conditions.

Advantages and disadvantages of direct labour

Advantages

The main advantages of direct labour may be said to be:

- *Greater construction co-ordination and control* – there is greater control and closer co-ordination of labour to the work, it provides considerable flexibility of working, and allows for rapid response to client's more urgent requirements.
- *More effective cost control* – financial control is improved and there is greater feedback concerning the resources used and performance achieved. There is, also, more effective information for compiling accounting records for future reference.
- *Better relationship between management (supervision) and the work-force* – as the labour force is in the direct employment of the client there is greater opportunity for effective liaison between supervisor and operative. There are open channels of communication in which information can pass and improved feedback to management.
- *Higher levels of performance and quality* – the overall performance of operatives, levels of workmanship and quality should be better, given that the labour force is of known abilities and skills.

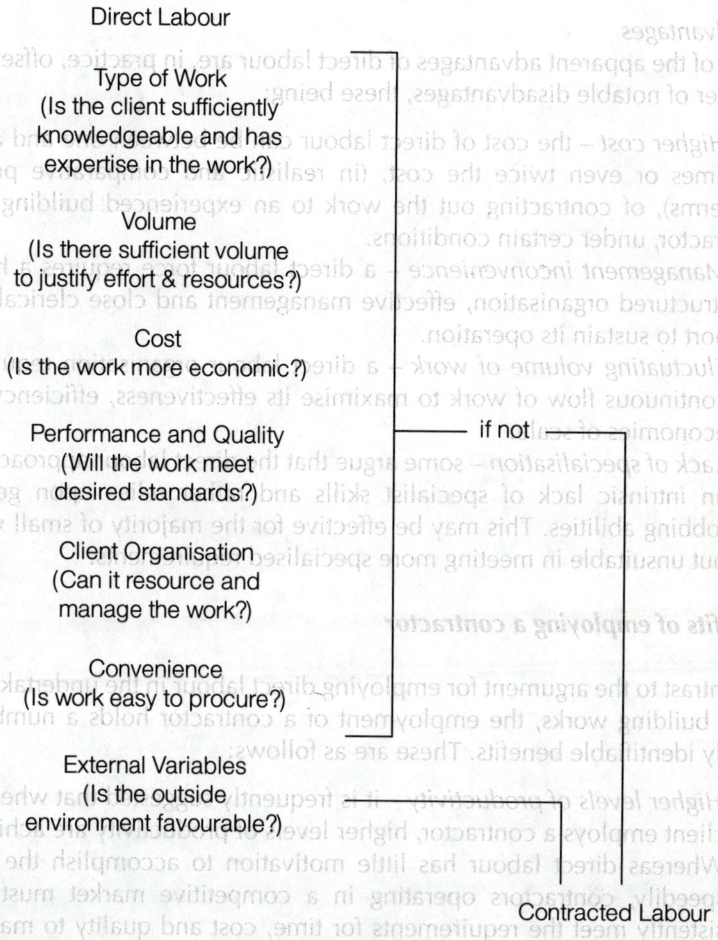

Direct Labour

Type of Work
(Is the client sufficiently
knowledgeable and has
expertise in the work?)

Volume
(Is there sufficient volume
to justify effort & resources?)

Cost
(Is the work more economic?)

Performance and Quality   if not
(Will the work meet
desired standards?)

Client Organisation
(Can it resource and
manage the work?)

Convenience
(Is work easy to procure?)

External Variables
(Is the outside
environment favourable?)

Contracted Labour

*Figure 3.1   Factors affecting the client's choice of direct labour or
contracted labour*

There can be greater risk when employing an outside contractor since the performance of the contractor is, or can be, unknown. In addition, there is employee identification with the organisation, giving greater potential for employer-led leadership and motivation.

- *More expeditious procurement* – the organisation of the work is direct and, therefore, faster. There is no tendering procedure or negotiation with contractors and the planning, approval and authorisation of the work is contained within a short chain of command and within the one organisation.

Disadvantages

Some of the apparent advantages of direct labour are, in practice, offset by a number of notable disadvantages, these being:

- *Higher cost* – the cost of direct labour can be between one and a half times or even twice the cost, (in realistic and comparative project terms), of contracting out the work to an experienced building contractor, under certain conditions.
- *Management inconvenience* – a direct labour force requires a highly structured organisation, effective management and close clerical support to sustain its operation.
- *Fluctuating volume of work* – a direct labour organisation requires a continuous flow of work to maximise its effectiveness, efficiency and economies of scale.
- *Lack of specialisation* – some argue that the direct labour approach has an intrinsic lack of specialist skills and rather relies upon general jobbing abilities. This may be effective for the majority of small works but unsuitable in meeting more specialised requirements.

Benefits of employing a contractor

In contrast to the argument for employing direct labour in the undertaking of small building works, the employment of a contractor holds a number of readily identifiable benefits. These are as follows:

- *Higher levels of productivity* – it is frequently suggested that where the client employs a contractor, higher levels of productivity are achieved. Whereas direct labour has little motivation to accomplish the work speedily, contractors operating in a competitive market must consistently meet the requirements for time, cost and quality to maintain their reputation and assure themselves of future work. This is particularly pertinent in the changing economic and political environments within which contractors must operate.
- *Specialist skills available* – the specialist skills and expertise of particular contractors is always available on demand, whereas a direct labour force may be able to handle general work competently but incapable of undertaking specialist work because it is beyond their abilities or resources.
- *Client pays the actual cost of the work* – with contracted labour, the client only pays for the work completed to the client's satisfaction. The client, generally, does not pay for totally non-productive time, although it is accepted that a certain degree of non-productive time will be covered by the contractor in the tender.
- *Reduced overheads* – the client has fewer overheads as, for example there are no stocks of materials or expensive construction plant and

equipment. The client only pays for the plant and materials used by the contractor.

In general, it is not easy, nor wise, to recommend either direct labour or contracted labour *per se*. There are many factors to consider surrounding the client organisation itself and these, combined with other circumstances, makes it unwise to suggest that one approach is better than another. Like so many aspects of construction it is really a case of weighing up the pros and cons in each situation and considering these in relation to the particular organisational circumstance. That said, there are circumstances in which the choice of contractor rather than direct labour, will show definite advantages.

As most client organisations will, more often than not, employ a contractor through choice to meet the nature of specific small works requirements, they will have to consider carefully those factors which influence the choice of contractor. Contractor selection therefore, rather like the argument for direct labour or contractor is an involved and frequently difficult issue.

3.2   Selection of the contractor

General

When a client procures small building works, the client will have a set of notional objectives which are put into a design perspective by a designer, architect, surveyor or engineer and which the contractor must fulfil in transforming that design into the finished building product. The difficulty for the client is in deciding which contractor is most likely to meet with the objectives of the work. In simple terms, the client must assess the contractor's capabilities, even though the client may not have employed that contractor before, and anticipate how well the contractor might meet the particular requirements for the small works. Even when selecting a contractor which has been employed previously, the client should still review the contractor's capabilities for the particular work, since all construction projects are by nature one-off and, therefore different. Changing circumstances within construction are ever present and such variability can be significant to contractor selection by a client.

On more extensive small works projects procured, for example on a lump sum contract basis, the client may well select a potential contractor through competitive tendering. The client can specify particular criteria within the contract documentation against which the client can quantitatively assess the tendering contractors. Small works of this nature tend, in the main, to be procured by selective tender or negotiation but even in the situation where the contractor is invited there is, obviously, client choice although this is based on qualitative rather than quantitative interpretation of the contractor's credentials.

The client, in seeking to select a small works building contractor, will consider the following capabilities of the contractor:

- Has the contractor the requisite organisational framework, structure and management to support the administration of the work?
- Has the contractor the necessary resources to carry out the work?
- Has the contractor a sufficiently sound financial base upon which to support the undertaking of the work?
- Will the contractor deploy and manage the organisational resources expeditiously and economically towards meeting the contractual requirements of the work?
- Has the contractor particular proposals for meeting the needs of the contract and are such proposals feasible and acceptable to the client? In addition, are the contractor's proposals better or worse than those of another contractor?

Such questions form the fundamental base upon which the client determines its choice of contractor. In answering these questions the client must collect and analyse a considerable amount of information about the contractor. Of the issues considered to be significant with regard to contractor selection and which are described in this section, the most important questions are:

- Is the contractor reputable?
- Is the contractor financially sound?
- Does the contractor have the necessary resources?
- What is the limit, range and scope of the contractor's normal work?

These and other important factors to be considered by the client are illustrated in Figure 3.2.

Contractor's reputation

In the view of most clients, the most significant influence in the selection of the contractor is likely to be the reputation of the contractor. The client will seek to establish a proven record of reliability, effectiveness and success in the sphere of potential employment. Whereas small clients may forgo the selection process for reasons of simplicity and economy, larger and, perhaps, more discerning client organisations are likely to appraise potential contractors through recommendation or previous experience of the contractor in question.

The client should seek to establish the following:

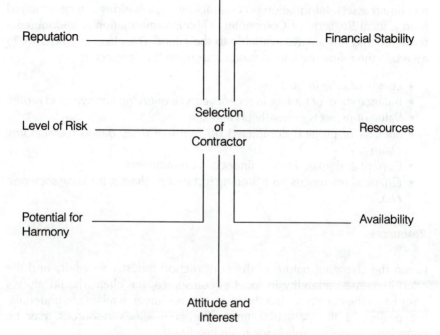

Figure 3.2 Factors upon which client's selection of contractor will be based

- The general reputation of the contractor on a local level or, if applicable, on a national level.
- A positive reference from clients who have, in the past, employed the contractor.
- Supporting evidence from previous contracts on which the contractor has been employed.
- The quality of the contractor's work by visiting and appraising completed projects.

Only after considering the contractor's general reputation in the local and, if appropriate, national construction community will the client engage in the detailed investigation of the contractor's organisation and financial standing.

Financial stability

The client should always consider the financial stability of the contractor's organisation. Whilst some contractors will be larger, operating on a national basis, others will be small locally-based and privately owned firms whose financial stability is variable and cannot be guaranteed. Small contractors, although financially sound, often operate on a minimum cashflow and have few liquid assets. Information on contracting organisations can be acquired from a local Registrar of Companies, although information is undoubtedly restricted and not always available to the client. The client should seek to ascertain the following information concerning the contractor:

- Length of time in business.
- Balance sheet of trading in recent years (*identifying turnover and profit*).
- Value of projects normally undertaken.
- Success of projects completed (*in terms of time, delays, outstanding claims*).
- Current anticipated future financial commitments.
- Financial references from funding institutions (*banks, building societies, etc*).

Resources

Given the changing nature of the construction industry generally and the often immense variability in local circumstance, the client should always ensure that the contractor has the necessary resources available to undertake the project at the particular time. The contractor's resources may be considered under the following main headings:

- *Physical* – place of business, offices, plant and equipment holding, fitting shop, stores and material.
- *Financial* – cashflow and liquid assets to finance the work on a day-to-day basis, (*in addition to those items considered under 'financial stability'*).
- *Personnel* – workforce complement, range of skills available and general ability to undertake the work.
- *Management* – range of management skills and supervisory capabilities, in particular in the technical area which will be needed to progress the works.

It is vitally important that the contractor can fulfil the requirements of all the aforementioned. There should be a good working balance within the contractor's organisation between all these aspects since the factors are not only important in their own right but are inextricably intertwined in their influence upon small building works.

Scope of the works

The client should seek to examine the kind of work that the contractor normally undertakes. This includes assessment of the:

- Type.
- Scale.
- Volume (*past and present*).
- Availability of specialist skills.

These aspects are influenced somewhat intrinsically by the contracting organisation, which may possibly be a general building contractor or specialist contractor. General building contractors vary considerably in many respects. Contractors tend to be categorised according to their size, financial standing and the range of projects they generally undertake. The client will essentially seek to equate the type and size of the contractor with the characteristics of the work. A client that is too small or, conversely, too large may be inappropriate for the resource requirement or economy of the work.

One must also achieve a balance between the degree of specialist skills available and the general skills available, since some small works will require both general and specialist input. The employment of a specialist contractor may be more costly than a general contractor and, therefore, if specialist skills are not really required to undertake the majority of the work they should be avoided. It is frequently more economic to re-design the small works so that they can be undertaken by a single general contractor than employ a specialist contractor, or moreover, multiple contractors, to fulfil the original design. An example might be modification of the foundation details such that the general contractor could easily undertake the work in preference to, say, a specialist piling contractor.

Other factors

The client must also consider a number of other factors in contractor selection, these include:

- Availability of the contractor.
- Degree of potential harmony between the client and contractor.
- Attitude and interest of the contractor.

The client must determine whether the contractor is available to undertake the work to the client's anticipated time schedule, an obvious but frequently understated factor. Whilst a large contractor should have little difficulty in scheduling the work, even if this means re-arranging other work to accommodate it, a smaller contractor may not have the same degree of flexibility. Small contractors tend to commit themselves to more work than a comfortable schedule permits in order to maintain work continuity and promote greater turnover, but this can lead to work congestion in the short-term and considerable backlog to future work.

If there is any likelihood of the contractor not being able to meet the client's time frame then the contractor should not be employed, even if this does mean that the client must pay more to another contractor. It is frequently more cost effective in the long-term to pay more to the contractor and get the work done on time than to penny-pinch on price, only to find the work is delayed or disrupted, resulting in extra and often uncontrollable cost.

Where a client has not employed the particular contractor before it is extremely difficult to anticipate if there will be, in practice, a close and harmonious relationship between the parties. The client should appreciate that some works depend, more than others, upon close liaison, open communication, mutual cooperation and the general level of understanding and harmony between the client and contractor. A harmonious relationship is more likely to present a project framework for success than one where constant disagreement pervades. Whether the client is comfortable and feels that trust can be placed in the contractor is an aspect which does, more often that not, play a significant part in the client's choice of contractor.

Very much in parallel with the degree of harmony, is the client's perception of the attitude and interest displayed by the contractor. It is essential that the client receives a positive and supportive response from the contractor. It is the general sense of professionalism demonstrated by the contractor which the client is seeking to identify. In addition to having the necessary technical, financial and management skills, the contractor must be able to produce good quality work, to time and to budget. If the contractor's attitude proves to be incongruous with the client's needs and objectives then the best will not be drawn out of either party and the execution of the small works is unlikely to be successful.

From the client's viewpoint, the better the client knows the contractor the easier it should be to manage the works. The client should always maintain a list of useable contractors based on the following basic information:

- Biographical profile.
- Areas and degree of specialisation.
- Location and spread of works.
- Size of contract undertaken.
- Skills and specialisations of operatives.
- Recent projects and performance profile.

The list of potential contractors should be maintained and updated regularly and new contractors should only be added to this list once they have been fully vetted by the client or his professional advisor.

3.3 Assessment of risk

General

When entering into any relationship and contract for work, whether the work is small and simple or extensive and complex, the client will assume some degree of risk. There is always a chance, however small, that something will go wrong on the project. This could be something brought about by the relationship skills demonstrated by the contractual parties, leading to disagreement, or it might be something extraneous over which there is little control such as inclement weather or totally unforeseen site conditions. Whatever the potential problem, the level of risk should be anticipated, where possible, so that catastrophic results are eliminated, or at least minimised.

Risk assessment is a crucial aspect of procurement and contract arrangement. It will be seen in Chapter 5 that the client must consider risk carefully when selecting a form of contract as this sets out the formal legal relationship between the two main parties. On a more general level, risk is an inherent aspect of getting any work done. There will always be risk and this must be accepted not only by the client but also by the contractor and any participant to the building process.

The client should consider:

(i) The level of risk involved in undertaking the work oneself since, even when direct labour is used, there is still some degree of risk to the client organisation.
(ii) The potential for increased risk by contracting-out the work and forming a relationship with another party and adopting a form of contract.

If, for example in the former situation, where a client employs direct labour to build a number of concrete machine bases to install new machinery, if the bases are incomplete when the machinery is delivered this could have serious knock-on effects for work progress.

It may then be seen in retrospect that the client would have been better contracting-out the work to achieve the objectives on time and eliminate any potential adverse ramifications. In the second situation, the risk is certain to increase as the client's organisation of the work is complicated with the interrelationship of the contractor's organisation. In many respects, the relationship is made more risky as the form of contract becomes more detailed and involved. Sometimes there will be just as much risk in having a contract as not having a contract.

Whilst contracts can never eliminate project difficulty they do serve to assist the resolution of difficulty when it occurs. It is frequently the contracts themselves that provide the basis for disagreement since contracts are not always clearly written nor easily understood. Ambiguity often results from the contract documentation itself.

Risk with direct labour

The client may, in practical terms, undertake the following (see Figure 3.3):

(i) Assess if it is possible to procure the work in-house to avoid entering into an agreement and relationship with a contractor and if it can then;

(ii) Determine the possible risk to the client organisation should the direct labour workforce not meet the requirements.

(iii) Have a contingency plan to manage the risk if anything should go wrong, (*this may involve re-arranging resources to complete the work or bringing in another contractor to complete unfinished works*).

Degree of Risk

Direct Labour	Contractor
Risk is known or more easily assessed	Risk is unknown and more difficult to assess
(abilities, skills and application of workforce is known beforehand)	*(abilities, skills and application of contractor may not be known)*
No outside relationship	Relationship with contractor
(no additional risk)	*(can increase the risk, in particular where parties have not worked together)*
No formal contract	Use of formal contract
(no additional risk)	*(may increase the risk if risk is poorly defined)*
Risk vested in one party	Contract assigns the risk
(client assumes all risks)	*(client or contractor may assume disproportionate level of risk)*

Figure 3.3   Degree of risk in employing direct labour or contractor

Risk with a contractor

Should the client have to contract out the work because it cannot be undertaken in-house, the degree of risk should be assessed by:

(i) Clearly defining the risk when entering into a relationship with the contractor.
(ii) Determining the degree of risk when using a standard form of building contract.
(iii) Establishing the allocation of the risk to the contractual parties.
(iv) Calculating the effect of risk relative to the level of involvement in the work by the client.
(v) Estimating how much trust may be placed in the contractor.
(vi) Determining a contingency plan to manage the work should anything go wrong with the chosen contractor, (for example, how easy would it be to obtain an alternative contractor, what is the effect on time, cost and quality, would the new contractor be reliable, etc.).

The problems of risk

The major problem with entering into any contractual arrangement is that the formal arrangement or standard form of building contract does not always clearly answer all the aforementioned questions which the client is likely to ask. In addition, the contract may convey its meaning in an ambiguous way, leaving both the client and contractor unsure as to their responsibilities. It is for this reason, if for no other, that the contractual parties have to, at times, consult with the legal profession to interpret the real meaning of the contract when disputes arise.

With the nature of small building works, it is unlikely that the relationship between the client and contractor and the form of contract would become the main source of difficulty since, by their very nature, small works will be small and uncomplicated and the arrangement and contract correspondingly so. Rather than worrying about the relationship or form of contract, the client should be more aware of the potential problems that arise due to the contractor failing to complete the agreed commitments (see Figure 3.4). The main types of problems arise from inadequacies in the contractor's organisation, these being:

- Insufficient experience and expertise to fulfil the technological requirements of the work.
- Lacking organisation and management skills to manage the work effectively and efficiently.
- Insufficient resources to carry out the work efficiently and cost effectively.

- Lacking financial stability to provide the necessary working cashflow.
- Inadequate planning and scheduling of workload to progress the work to the client's requirements among the contractor's other commitments.
- Too small an organisation to provide adaptability to changing circumstance if problems arise.

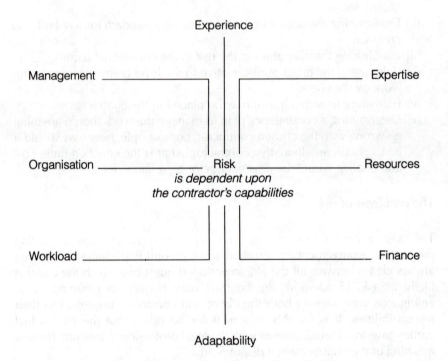

Figure 3.4 Capabilities of the contractor upon which the client's risk is dependent

Insurance

In all situations the client must ensure that the work, however small, be covered by some measure of insurance. On larger projects it is usual for all parties to be fully covered for their professional liabilities. On small works it would be wise for the client to take out a mutual insurance policy to cover both the client and the contractor against third party liability. From the client's viewpoint it is essential to safeguard the work since the most important aspect to the client is to get the work done quickly, efficiently and successfully.

Acceptance of risk

Risk is always inherent in any construction project. Whilst it is reasonable to suggest that the degree of risk will increase with the technical complexity, extent and cost of the work, this does not infer that small works have a lesser degree of risk. It is simply that the risk, in absolute terms, will be less but, of course, the risk should be regarded as proportional to the nature of the works. In principle, the same types of problems that can afflict major construction projects can affect small works projects. The important issues to appreciate are:

- Risk will occur.
- The client and contractor know and accept that risk will occur.
- Whilst most risk can be foreseen and calculated there will always be some unforeseen or incalculable risk.
- Contingencies should always be considered in advance so that action is readily available to meet the risk.
- Good risk management relies upon being prepared and not scrambling for a resolution once a difficulty emerges.

4 Procurement and Contract Arrangement

4.1 The basis of procurement and contract arrangement

General

The client, when seeking to procure and authorise the undertaking of small building works, has a variety of procurement and contract arrangements available. Essentially, any arrangement represents a formal relationship between the two main parties involved in the work, the client and the contractor. The various standard forms of building contract used to confirm the legal relationship are reviewed in Chapter 5. The main differences between the various types of procurement and contractual arrangement feature in the variations of methods used to describe, measure, value and discharge the works. Forms of approach can accommodate a wide range of small building works, from individual construction projects entailing little complexity and with few demands upon resources, to more intricate and demanding construction which require greater, technical and managerial expertise. Works such as these may be arranged informally with a minimum of interrelations between the client and contractor and with little contract documentation, or be procured on a formal level under explicit forms of contract with considerable documentation. Irrespective of differing circumstances, there is usually an appropriate method available.

The nature of small building works and their management will differ among client organisations according to their: knowledge and experience of small works; their own internal organisation; the management philosophy they hold and systems they use; the commercial markets in which they operate; and the degree of risk they are prepared to assume. Although such organisational factors justify consideration, greater influence is exerted by the characteristics of the work itself. The choice of contractor may, in itself, be sufficient to select the form of procurement and contract arrangement as some contractors specialise in particular types and values of work which determines, somewhat inherently, the form of contract and interrelationship between the parties.

48

Characteristics of the work

The main characteristics of the work influencing procurement approach and contract arrangement are;

(i) *Type* – complexity of the work in terms of its technical design, materials, construction and the requirement for management, supervision and administration.

(ii) *Scale* – magnitude of the work in terms of cost value, efficacy of measurement and level of financial management required.

(iii) *Volume* – number of similar works to be carried out, degree of continuity and potential benefit through economies of scale.

The client will, in addition to appreciating the type, scale and volume of small building works, determine the procurement and contract arrangement with consideration to other factors. These include: time; cost; quality; work locations; availability of the contractor; and indeed, all relevant factors that should be considered before embarking on any building project.

Types of arrangement

The following approaches represent the most widely used and accepted methods of procurement and contract arrangement for small building works;

- Works order.
- Daywork order.
- Measured Term. (*Often termed: 'Schedule Contract'*)
- Minor Measured Term.
- Daywork Term. (*Often termed: 'Cost Reimbursement Contract'*)
- Annual Term.
- Minor lump-sum fixed price.

Each of these arrangements is described and discussed in detail from both the client's and contractor's viewpoint and the relative advantages and disadvantages of each are identified and reviewed. There is little doubt for the client that there is considerable scope for encouraging improved efficiency and greater economy through the better management of small works. The factor which is perhaps of most significance is the form of procurement and contract arrangement, as this sets up the basis of relationships upon which success of the works depend.

4.2 Individual small works (*works order, daywork order*)

In the main, a client will procure the undertaking of individual small works, (sometimes referred to as 'jobbing' works although more accurately described as 'ordered' works), through the issue of a written authorisation or order to the contractor. This authorisation commonly takes one of two forms, the issue of a

(i) Works order.
(ii) Daywork order.

A *works order* is an authorisation by the client, issued to the contractor, detailing the work to be undertaken. In general, the value of the work will be low and issued for minor new building work, an alteration to an existing building or structure, a repair, or for minor and unscheduled maintenance tasks. It is usual for the order to be accompanied by a description of the works, a drawing and a specification, with the order being issued on a fixed price basis.

A *Daywork order* is also an authorisation by the client to the contractor to undertake the work. Unlike the works order which is a fixed price, a daywork order is determined on a 'cost plus' basis. This enables the contractor to charge the client for the full cost of labour, plant and materials and include an additional element of cost for the contractor's overheads and profit.

Works order

A works order may be procured on a competitive basis, through obtaining tendered bids from various contractors, or on a non-competitive basis. When non-competitive orders are issued by the client, the value of the work is likely to be low and hence the work will be trusted to one contractor, normally one the client has employed on a previous occasion. Beyond a pre-determined cost limit, the client is more ready to obtain quotations, (cost estimates), from a number of contractors on the basis that competitiveness will reduce the cost of the work and increase obtainable value for money. An implication of non-competitive procurement is that the client does not effectively 'shop around' and can become too accustomed to one contractor, one mode of operation and one pricing policy.

With a competitive approach, difficulties may also arise. It is expensive for the contractor, even in a small works situation, to prepare a truly competitive quotation and the likely additional cost incurred by the contractor in producing the bid will undoubtedly be reflected in the price. The lower the small works value, the greater the proportion of additional cost from tendering will be, as the tender cost is likely to be rounded-up considerably before being added to the estimated net costs of the works. On an estimated net cost of, say, two hundred pounds, rather than add ten per cent of this value to cover tender preparation, giving a total estimated cost of two hundred and twenty pounds, the total cost might be rounded up to two hundred and fifty pounds, making the additional percentage for tender preparation twenty per cent. For this reason, it is sensible for the client not to set the works order cost limit too low when procuring on a non-competitive basis. In contrast, the client must also safeguard against setting a works order cost limit which is too high. When the cost limit is excessive there can be a danger that the client will accept any quotation, almost with complacency, simply because the cost is below the set limit. In such an event, the client cannot assess if value for money is being obtained and, in reality, it is likely that value for money will not be fully realised.

It is also important for the client to set a realistic limit on the cost of orders, not too high, not too low, to avoid the practice of splitting up the work over a number of separate works orders. Should the works be split in this way, it makes administration difficult with possible detriment to close cost control. Although in practice multiple tasks are often instructed under the one order, in a well managed situation, one works order should represent one small works item.

Where a works order approach is to be used, the client should, ideally, issue the order on a competitive basis to obtain a range of cost alternatives which may facilitate improved economy. The client should seek quotations from at least three building contractors to encourage competition and a keen price. This rule of thumb will, however, depend upon the type, scale and volume of the work. Non-competitive procurement would almost always be preferred for very minor works where minuscule scale would simply make tendering inherently cost prohibitive.

The client may issue a works order to a contractor who acts directly upon that order, or alternatively, the client may issue a Request for Quotation and upon receipt of a tender bid, issue a corresponding works order to authorise the work. Adopting the latter approach, the client may issue requests for quotation to a number of contractors and issue the works order to the selected contractor alone. When the client is dealing with a single contractor, the former approach is usually acceptable but when more than one contractor is involved, the latter is preferred to remove any ambiguity that may arise between a quotation request and an order, since the works order is, by definition, an instruction to undertake the works and forms an agreement between the client and contractor.

In general, works orders should specify a title for the work to be carried out, a description, its location, an estimate of cost and all necessary details of the client and the contractor, (*address, telephone number, contact name*). It is usual for the reverse side of the works order form itself to state standard terms and conditions, (*and any special conditions*), under which the contractor should be prepared to undertake the works. The detail of contractual terms and conditions will, again, depend upon the type, scale and volume of the works but, in general, the greater the specialisation required the more precise and detailed the conditions will be. The vast majority of these general conditions will be second nature to contractors who regularly undertake such works, but nevertheless, the terms and conditions should always be reviewed. Likewise, the quotation or tender submitted by the contractor may specify standard conditions under which the contractor accepts the client's work. Again, the client should carefully review the conditions to see that there is no conflict with the client's view and assessment of the work.

Any quotations failing to meet with the client's requirements should be rejected or returned to the contractor for review and possible re-submission. On no account should a client accept a quotation which fails to satisfy the genuine requirements, simply because it is easier to accept than reject the bid or because it may involve additional time, effort and expense. Compromise at this stage may invite difficulty later in the construction process.

Where the work to be undertaken is unclear or of an unknown nature, allowances should be made by the client and the contractor forewarned in order that potential extra cost may be incorporated in the price. When the client can approach only one contractor, as might be the case when procuring specialist trades, there may be no alternative but to accept that contractor on the contractor's own terms. Once more, the client must consider carefully any reciprocal terms and conditions to the client's own, submitted with the contractor's quotation.

Daywork order

The daywork order is one of the most widely used methods of procurement for small works. The daywork order is used most appropriately when the nature and extent of the proposed works cannot be precisely determined or when the duration of the works cannot accurately be predicted. For the contractor, the daywork order ensures that all labour, plant, and materials used, together with overheads and profit, are allowed for. Hence the contractor will not be out of pocket. For the client, it means that, in theory, only the work completed plus minimum additions are paid for. If the client issues an uncosted works order, which is sometimes the case, then, in effect, it becomes a daywork order as the contractor will almost certainly price the work on an estimated daywork (*cost plus*) basis.

The issue of dayworks orders, and for that matter works orders, should be treated with considerable respect by the client's quantity surveyor, (if employed), or finance department. All daywork must be carefully administered, properly supervised and accurately measured to ensure that the work progresses to an appropriate time schedule, is performed to satisfactory quality levels and is priced by the contractor, so reflecting the genuine claim for resources used.

Daywork ordering, whilst being one of the most popular methods of procuring small works by clients does have a great many issues to consider, not least of which being that it is heavily reliant upon the integrity and honesty of the contractor to accomplish the work efficiently and cost effectively. Clearly, the contractor has no real incentive to carry out the work quickly as payment is based upon labour time expended and, therefore, procrastination and inefficiency can, and does, frequently lead to the client over-paying for the work. This can be further exacerbated if the contractor uses over-specified materials and uneconomic construction plant as the client will, again, incur overpayment through the additional overheads and profit applicable on those unnecessary materials and plant items. The general extravagance of contractors in undertaking small works is clearly understandable as the business of the contractor is ostensibly to make a profit. Any exaggeration of the time spent on the work will increase the value of the account rendered and thereby the profit.

Whilst there are undoubted instances of unscrupulous contractors falsifying labour returns for daywork, even the most honest and reliable contractors are likely, at some time, to over-claim hours spent on a job, whether this be deliberate or otherwise. From the client's viewpoint, it should always be accepted that the more unscrupulous contractor will, 'given an inch, take a mile'. The more knowledgeable and concerned client will take steps to mitigate this possibility. The daywork order should predetermine, by estimate, usually from experience, the likely duration of the work. This can be specified in manhours which can then be developed into an outline cost target. To minimise excessive costs, an individual daywork order should be subject to a upper cost limit with an investigative mechanism introduced to extract information on any claim made where the final cost exceeds the cost limit. It will be seen subsequently, that on Measured Term Contracts and Daywork Term Contracts that the client's quantity surveyor may impose such a system to verify excessive costs claimed against individual orders in the contractor's valuation. It should also be common practice that the client or his representative carries out random visits to observe the works in progress, during which the labour, plant and material resources can be assessed and, if necessary, be formally measured and recorded to assist in the verification of the daywork account at a later date.

Despite such attempts to verify the true status of the works, the client must accept that exaggeration will feature in the contractor's assessment of labour, plant and materials used. It will always be human nature to 'round-up' the manhours expended when compiling the foreman's or supervisor's labour returns, which again, are likely to be rounded-up on the daywork account. It is not always that the contractor is seeking to cheat the client, but more a case of the contractor erring on the cautious side in calculating the level of expenditure.

It is frequent and unfortunate for the client that a large proportion of small works fall into the category of daywork or lie in the grey area between measurable work and daywork. Whenever a job leans toward a daywork orientation the likelihood is that the contractor will press for daywork status so as to minimise the potential risk in undertaking the work. If the client cannot accurately predict the time and cost parameters for the work then the client is almost disposed, psychologically at least, to deem the job as daywork. Of course, many small works can only be carried out on a daywork basis, particularly if the work is very small or extraneous influences such as geographic location or difficult working conditions exist. A daywork basis may be the only way in which the client can make the work attractive to the contractor.

It is often on small, unspecified or isolated works that the client is in danger to the more opportunist contractor. The mark up on cost and profit is likely to be much higher than on a normal daywork job. This is easily rationalised from the contractor's viewpoint, since the work may incur additional expense in, for example, travelling to the work. To the client, however, the work may appear excessively expensive than a comparable job nearer home.

Even on works such as those mentioned, the client should make every effort to supervise and administer the work if the client is to avoid being taken advantage of or at least the feeling that he has been taken advantage of; the latter is often more important to a client. In difficult circumstances it is beneficial for the client and contractor to discuss the work in detail before commencement to air any opposing views and avoid any grievances occurring later during construction, measurement or valuation.

Application of works orders and daywork orders to direct labour small works

The aforementioned discussion has presupposed that there is a contract arrangement between a client and a contractor. The principles and procedures for procuring works orders and daywork orders are equally applicable to a client organisation when it uses direct labour. The use of such orders is essential to establishing a structure and system of management within the organisation within which small works can be effectively planned, procured and carried out. The issue of orders within the direct labour context follows the same pattern as that established for contracted labour. Obviously, the orders are issued on a non-competitive basis as tendering is not necessary. The orders also serve to provide essential budgetary control which applies equally to the control of direct labour as it does to contracted labour.

Most clients will treat the direct labour complement within their organisation as a self-supporting and commercial entity and the rigour invoked by the works order and dayworks order system demands that careful financial management becomes a feature of its operation. In this way, the direct labour commitment can be compared with contracted labour to ensure that it is providing the client organisation with real value for money and does not become a wasteful burden that has to be financially carried by the client. If it costs more to employ the direct labour force than contracted labour then the organisation would simply be better off to contract the works. For this reason, the direct labour force should always be thought of by the client organisation as a commercial enterprise requiring skilled and careful management. Using works orders and daywork order systems gives the client organisation the basic foundation upon which to ensure that this is successfully achieved.

Advantages of the 'order' system

It is clear that the organisation of small works on a works order basis or daywork order arrangement has some distinct advantages for the client. Similarly, if managed ineffectively, there are also identifiable disadvantages. These can be summarised for works orders and daywork orders respectively, as follows;

Works order
The advantages are:

- The easy placing of orders, where orders may be placed verbally and often by telephone.
- There is no complex documentation, as contracts, if used, tend to be simple and straightforward; simple drawings, specifications and instructions are generally preferred.
- The cost is based on a fixed price, which is useful in the close budgetary control of the work.
- Work can be let on a competitive or non-competitive basis, cost benefit analysis is available to the client if cost is paramount.
- The formal arrangement is uncomplicated, with the general terms and conditions specified on the reverse of the works order issued to the contractor.
- The method is applicable to direct labour or contracted labour, with similar procedures being used for either approach.

The disadvantages are:

- Client may become accustomed to one contractor, one mode of operation and one pricing policy.
- Considerable work and effort is needed to obtain competitive quotations and a competitive approach may be cost prohibitive, a non-competitive basis being more appropriate for daywork.
- Competitive bids can be over-priced as considerable 'mark-up' on contractor's tender bids, to cover tender costs, is commonplace.
- Client can become complacent at fixed-priced bids with the tendency towards automatically processing the order for ease and convenience.

- Client may be taken advantage of by enterprising or unscrupulous contractor seeking to maximise profit margin.

Daywork orders
The advantages are:

- They are widely used, and well understood and accepted by both clients and contractors.
- That orders are easily placed, often verbally and with a minimum of paperwork.
- There is no complex documentation as formal arrangement is uncomplicated with simple drawings, specifications and instructions being preferred.
- Preferred method when the client cannot specify the work accurately due to, perhaps, its unknown nature or indeterminate quantity or where there is little efficacy of measurement.
- Useful method of engaging a contractor where the nature of work is essentially unattractive.
- The method is available to direct labour or contracted labour with similar procedures being used for either approach.

The disadvantages are:

- There is a variable cost, as price is based on the labour, plant and material cost plus overhead and profit elements.
- That burdensome administration is needed, to ensure that costs claimed by the contractor are genuine and accurate.
- That the process is reliant upon the integrity and honesty of the contractor and can be prone to misuse by an enterprising or unscrupulous contractor.
- There is no incentive for the contractor to carry out the work speedily and can be liable to procrastination since price is largely based on manhours expended.
- There is a likelihood of over-costing as the contractor may 'mark-up' hours on labour returns, over-specify materials and plant items so increasing the profit level.
- That unattractive projects must be carried out on a daywork basis to attract the interest of a contractor and the contractor may, therefore, be able to charge the client an exorbitant price.

Whilst there are some distinct pitfalls in procuring small works on a works order or daywork basis, it is also clear that there is equally some merit in their general application. Both clients and contractors are familiar with the pro's and con's and there is a general acceptance that there must be give and take by the parties if the procedures are to succeed. Most contractors know that there is some leeway in the system within which some advantage may be taken of the client, and equally, clients recognise this leeway but accept it, but only within their own well defined limits.

Both parties also accept equally, that the plain fact is that, in some instances, there can be no viable alternative but to procure and undertake small works on a purely jobbing basis or using works orders or daywork orders. For the small, isolated project, any and all encumbrances must be shouldered simply to get the job done. For the more complex works or multiple jobbing works, the basic work order or daywork order arrangement may be less acceptable with greater formality being needed. This is where a Measured Term Contract, Daywork Term Contract and other specialised forms of contractual arrangement come into their own.

Detail of works or daywork order

The nature, detail and format of works orders and daywork orders will, obviously, vary among clients and similarly, operating procedures and administrations will differ among contractors. Nevertheless, there are basic minimum guidelines to the type of information that should be prescribed on such orders. This information will, ideally, include the following:

- Order number.
- Name and address of the contractor. (*Omitted on a term contract.*)
- Job title.
- Date of issue.
- Description of the work.
- Level of priority.
- Date for commencement.
- Anticipated date for completion.
- Reference of the issuing officer.
- Name and address of issuing organisation. (*Omitted on term contract.*)
- Estimated or anticipated manhours content.
- Estimate of materials and plant.
- Actual resource expenditure (filled in upon completion of the works for record purposes).

On a works order or daywork order, an example of which is presented in Appendix 1, the description given by the client is the main source of information, although it will be supplemented by drawings and a specification. The detail should, therefore, be as full as possible. Where repetitive works occur, there should be a standardised description that conveys the same meaning each time it is used, that is, an identified description for an identified job. The description should always be accompanied by an estimate of the expected cost for labour, plant and materials and sufficient space left to provide the actual resources and cost to be recorded for future reference. The nature of small works will, however, not always allow detailed description nor accurate assessment and this is, of course, why the detail presented is frequently vague, leaving opportunity for ambiguity and problems to ensue.

When procuring small works, on a works order or daywork order basis, it is, in general, beneficial to the client to:

(i)   Let the work on a competitive basis, (*where appropriate*), by obtaining a number of quotations to realistically appreciate, if not minimise the cost.
(ii) Specify the outline cost to establish budgetary control.
(iii) State expected duration of the work, taking into account any potential difficulties and allowing contingencies for unexpected problems.
(iv) Always use a written order, rather than rely on verbal communication and instruction.
(v)   Monitor and approve the jobs as works proceed and upon final completion.
(vii) Verify the contractor's valuations by random spot checks of the works in progress and when they are completed and remeasure if necessary.

4.3   Measured Term Contract

(*Also known as a Schedule Contract or Measured Value Contract*)

Definition

Where a client has a considerable number of small works to be carried out, or is involved in the regular and continuous process of procuring small works, alterations, repairs and minor maintenance, a *Measured Term Contract* is often employed. In essence, a measured term contract is a formal arrangement between the client and a single contractor in which all works of a similar and measurable type and nature and which fall within specified cost parameters are carried out within the one contract. This contract is for a fixed duration, (*term*), and may be let by the client on a non-competitive basis, although a competitive approach is preferred and most often used. The term of the contract can vary according to the scale and nature of the works and the client's preference for continuity or change, but a normal duration for a measured term contract may be from one to five years, with three years being the norm. Longer term contracts tend to have review mechanisms in-built to its arrangement so that an annual assessment can be made beyond the initial three year period.

A measured term contract is the most appropriate form of procurement for small building works in the following circumstances:

- Where there is a continuous need for small building works by the client.
- Where there is sufficient continuity of work to facilitate efficiency and economy.
- Where the client requires a rapid response to work demands.

Schedule of rates

Term contracts are structured around a standardised and pre-costed schedule of rates which is issued to all prospective tenderers. (*Hence the name Schedule Contract.*) The competitive element of measured term contract bids is reflected in the different percentage price adjustments made to the schedule by the various tenderers. These price adjustments represent the different trading overheads and profit levels required by the contractors.

In simple terms, the contractor tendering for the work analyses the schedule of rates, together with the terms and conditions provided by the client, and calculates a percentage adjustment that will, when added to (or subtracted from in some instances) the schedule of rates, provide sufficient reimbursement to the contractor for organisational and operational needs whilst the bid remains on a measured and competitive basis. It is easy for the client to assess the percentage adjustment, (*often referred to as the 'mark up'*), included by the contractor on the basic schedule. The price adjustment will vary among contractors, depending upon many and diverse factors, but a genuine and acceptable adjustment would be clearly seen by the client compared with a grossly over-estimated and speculative bid.

While the use of measured term contracts is usually associated with major client organisations holding large building capital assets in both the public and private sectors, where small works account for a considerable proportion of their building related activity, in theory no client organisation is precluded from developing a schedule of rates for their own use. Although major clients may like to develop their own schedules to meet the precise and unique characteristics of their own organisation and needs, generic schedules also exist.

The Department of the Environment (DoE), Property Services Agency (PSA) and the Society of Chief Quantity Surveyors in Local Government (SCQSLG), in collaboration with the Building Employer's Confederation (BEC) have, over many years developed various schedules of rates and terms and conditions of contract which are applicable to the type, scale and volume of works procured by many users. Such schedules, adopted by many organisations, as a useful basis for measured term works, have been tried and tested over a prolonged period as a general framework within which the detail can be adapted by the user to meet the most appropriate needs of the organisation.

The benefits of a standard schedule of rates are well recognised in, for example, the PSA schedule. These are as follows:

- It is a most comprehensive schedule of rates for building works.
- The format is clear, concise and displays common arrangement to other project documentation such as the Standard Method of Measurement of Building Works.
- Detail concerning labour items exceeds those of the Standard Method of Measurement.
- The schedule is essentially a contract document in its own right.
- It provides a facility for up-dating percentages to be applied in a single format.
- The schedule is constantly revised and re-issued for up-to-date guidance.
- The PSA schedule is one of the uniform schedule of rates recommended to local authorities by the Building Employer's Confederation.
- The schedule is well recognised and respected in the private sector.
- Conditions of contract that accompany the schedule are well tried and well recognised in application.

Any schedule of rates fulfils a number of functions. It serves in:

- *Assessment of tenders* – schedule allows a comparison between different tender bids in the different percentage adjustments.
- *Forms the basis of payment* – schedule sets the basis for measuring and costing all work undertaken on the contract.
- *Allows budget planning* – it enables the client to estimate the cost of on-going and future works and plan accordingly.

The precise content, detail and format of a schedule of rates will vary in meeting the needs of the client and the project on which the schedule will be used. Most schedules will however, usually have three main sections:

(i) Preliminaries – defining the scope of the contract and any particular details pertinent to the contractual relationship and functioning of the client and contractor.

(ii) Preambles – describing the specifications for materials and workmanship.

(iii) Rates for Items of Work – descriptions of all work items and the costed process, subject to the percentage adjustments.

Two types of schedule are generally available for use, these are:

(i) *Detailed Schedule* – containing individual items of work for separate tasks, the job being priced by building up the various separate tasks.

(ii) *Composite Schedule* – containing items for work covering a range of possible activities involved in undertaking the work.

There are a number of advantages and disadvantages associated with the utilisation of either schedule and, in general, selection will be based upon the degree of accuracy required in measuring and pricing the work and the level of measurement and associated administration between the two types. For example, a detailed schedule would be advised on higher value works with disparate nature whereas a composite schedule would suffice on lower value uniform works, but selection will always be dependent on particular circumstances, so one should not generalise.

A client must also consider the pertinence of choosing a standard off-the-peg schedule or creating one's own schedule of rates. There are advantages and disadvantages with each and for this reason alone many clients choose to create a hybrid version exemplifying the virtues of each.

The advantages of a standard schedule are:

- Availability – readily available.
- Simplicity – content is simple and understandable.
- Economy – relatively cheap contract document.
- Familiarity – known to clients and contractors.
- Recognition and acceptance – known, tried and tested.
- Understandable and practical – simple to put into practice.

Advantages of a client-developed schedule are:

- Continuity – follows past and known practice.
- Comprehensive – detail can be as required.
- Brevity – document can be concise and specific.
- Compatibility – easily adaptable to existing procedures.

The main difficulties with adopting the latter form of schedule is the unfamiliarity of the form to the contractor, unless he has worked with the client previously. There will need to be a period of learning before the contractor can use the particular and specialised schedule. This problem is alleviated with a standard schedule, provided of course that the contractor has used this before. Again, the choice of schedule must be carefully considered by the client depending upon prevailing circumstances and a generalised choice should be avoided.

Tendering and tender documentation

An effective measured term contract, like all forms of contract arrangement, depends upon clear and unambiguous tender documentation. The tender documents must contain all the necessary details of the proposed works in order that the contractor may anticipate and consider all aspects of the work which are pertinent to preparing a comprehensive priced tender.

The difficulty in tender preparation for small works under a term contract is that the works themselves are often undefined and unspecified at the time of tender. Although there will be a general awareness of the broad type of the proposed works, the precise detail and scale of individual jobs remains materially unknown and is only revealed during the term of the contract as individual work orders are issued by the client. In some respects, this feature of uncertainty brought to bear by measured term contracts is one reason why particular contractors specialise in such works. If the contractor has worked with clients on term contracts previously then they are in the advantageous position of being able to anticipate, from previous works, the type, scale and detail of the range of works expected. A tenderer, new to the concept of measured term contracts, whilst having the capability to undertake the works when requested, may not be able to anticipate the works clearly beforehand.

Although the individual jobs to be carried out under the term contract cannot be specified at the time of tender, their likely magnitude and general characteristics will be known by the client. From this knowledge, the client can specify the Estimated Contract Value, (ECV), or, more usually the Estimated Annual Value, (EAV), to the tenderer. Whilst there is likely to be some fluctuation in the ECV or EAV, the estimate made is usually sufficient for the contractor to calculate the resource commitment to the contract and price accordingly. In practice, most, if not all, contractors will welcome additional works as it will have few implications to the overhead and profit calculations, but, will be unhappy when the ECV or EAV falls as this will affect the predetermined profit margin.

There may be some danger to the contract if the client increases the workload substantially during the term, in particular if the contractor is inexperienced in handling sudden fluctuations in work pressure. Many contractors are extremely competent at fulfilling their basic requirements under the term conditions and can accommodate a modest workload fluctuation of, say, up to fifteen per cent of the ECV or EAV. There will, however, be an optimum point beyond which the contractor becomes over-stretched with the potential consequence that some of the works or, indeed, all works may suffer. The client must, therefore, not expect too much from the contractor beyond the predetermined volume and value of the term works. Should the works increase dramatically, the client should be pre-pared to renegotiate the term contract with the contractor who can then bring on to the site additional resources to fulfil the expanded commitment. Alternatively, the client may choose to subdivide the one contract between two contractors to form two separate term contracts.

On expansive works where, for example, a petrochemical client organ-isation has a requirement for small works across a large plant complex, it is frequently the case that the construction work will be split amongst a considerable number of contractors with each operating under a separate term agreement. A general contractor may undertake the building con-struction aspect of the small works let under one term contract, whilst other trades such as scaffolding, plumbing, flooring and painting are contracted under individual and quite separate term contracts to specialist trade contractors. Although the client has the benefit of securing the services of experienced specialists in their fields, there can be inherent difficulties in the co-ordination and control of the works when so many different contractors operate simultaneously across the general construction site.

It is not uncommon to find the general contractor standing idle for some considerable time whilst the scaffolder erects the temporary workstages, or that the general contractor must discontinue the work while another contractor installs fixtures and fittings. Since the client procures the work of the general contractor and the individual specialist contractors himself through separate term contracts and the works order system and not the general contractor employing these specialists as subcontractors, the client assumes a difficult and onerous responsibility to ensure that the various contractors complete their works to the required standard whilst not obstructing the other contractors.

When inviting tenders for the term contract the client will specify the schedule of rates upon which the tender is to be based. This could be a schedule developed exclusively by the client, a generic schedule adapted to the works, or be a standard schedule such as the PSA schedule of rates. The client will, usually provide a copy of the schedule or instruct the tenderer to obtain the appropriate schedule from a designated source. The schedule of rates will follow a pattern of broad trade tasks, for example, demolitions, alterations, excavations, and the like. No drawings are provided for the work because the technological detail and extent of individual works is unknown at the time of tender. It is usual for the client to provide the contractor with a general site location plan if the proposed works are within a defined area and also typical or standard construction details if these are available. This minimum detail and information will afford the contractor the opportunity of pricing into the tender any costs relating to the geographical location of the site and additional costs to meet particular construction requirements. Costs could, of course, vary considerably, with the location affecting travelling time of labour and the transportation of materials being common examples.

The expected location of the contractor's temporary site organisation will be specified, again so the contractor may price in the tender all anticipated costs for site accommodation, compounds, storage, workshops and the like. Costs of this nature are not borne by the client directly but must be allowed for by the contractor within the make-up of the price percentage added to the schedule of rates. A tenderer could become, therefore, uncompetitive through the inclusion of excessive overheads to cover a grandiose site facility. This is yet a further example of where the existing term contractor scores an advantage over a new, or perhaps naive, tenderer. The experienced contractor will know what precise resources are needed for a temporary site organisation and will price this realistically rather than over-specify.

On more considerable small works term contracts this aspect is sometimes made irrelevant through client provision of site accommodation and compounds. Where a client is dissatisfied with the work of a term contractor it is easy to remove that contractor but, where the contractor has provided his own site facility, a replacement contractor and new temporary site organisation may have significant cost implications for the client. In practice, both the client and contractor realise this aspect is important and often a relationship is sustained despite apparent shortcomings.

Pricing and cost fluctuation

The client must, as with any other form of contract arrangement, specify expected working hours, overtime working and other factors which bear some influence upon the contractor's assessment of pricing policy. The contractor may, for example, price into the schedule allowances for over-time working where extra costs may be one and a half times or twice the normal daily labour and trade rates or may come to an agreement with the client that additional working will be priced on a daywork basis. If this is predetermined and agreed there are usually few problems.

A prominent issue that does arise on term contracts is the unavoidable and indeterminate cost increases to labour, plant and materials that occur during the term of the contract. Historically, this aspect presented little difficulty as costs, in general, were slow to rise, but in more uncertain economic times they must be taken into account by the contractor if he is not to be caught out by sudden fluctuations due to economic, political, environmental and other significant factors. As it is almost impossible for the contractor to anticipate the effect of such fluctuations and unreasonable of the client to expect otherwise, measured term contracts tend to include a price fluctuation formula to accommodate increased costs. This adjusts the prices of com-pleted works claimed for within the contractor's interim valuations and brings the costs inline with genuine and current values.

The price fluctuation, or percentage addition is worked out on known increases in the labour and material rates for the previous month and included in the current monthly interim valuation. The adjustment per-centages are specified in a table of adjusted figures calculated by such bodies as the PSA, in a similar way to figures indexed by the National Economic Development Office, (NEDO), for application to increased cost formulae used under a Joint Contracts Tribunal (JCT) Standard Form of Building Contract. The adjustment can be a whole contract adjustment or apply to specific aspects of the works. Although such index price fluctuation formulae appear complex at first glance, they are well accepted and easy to administer. They take into account any fluctuation that could not be perceived at the time of tender.

Similarly, as major clients use standard measured term contract docu-mentation and schedules of rates over a period of many years they need to update the schedules at regular intervals. Again rather than re-calculate the great many rates specified in the schedule, increases such as inflationary adjustments will be added by means of a price fluctuation percentage. Irrespective of the way in which a price fluctuation is accommodated, the crucial issue is that the contractor should be told quite unambiguously how the price is to be calculated in the tender and under what terms and conditions.

While indexed adjustments warrant that the prices given in the schedule are current, the contractor's estimator must ensure that all other costs that will be incurred in running the contract are covered and that all possible additions to these costs are also included. There may be, for example, additional costs resulting from prolonged travelling time, if the source of labour changes, or there might be an exorbitant rise in telephone service charges. It is the contractor's responsibility to price for these items and include allowances for such when tendering.

Milne[1], when reviewing price fluctuations in building maintenance work, raises an important issue to consider.

> The updating percentage which will be applied to any individual work order is that current at the date of issue of the order and the tenderer has to allow for any possible increase in the cost of the labour and materials applicable to that order during the period of time taken to complete the work.

Although this is important, in practice this issue may be made somewhat irrelevant, as the vast majority of small works will be completed quickly following the receipt of the works order from the client. It would be most unlikely that a price fluctuation would affect a single item of work specified on one work order. There is, however, one situation when the issue may arise and that is when there is an excessive duration of the work due to some problem beyond the control of the contractor. Such instances are fortunately rare but the client should nonetheless issue orders on the basis that the work they cover will take only a short time to complete. Should a longer duration be anticipated the client should issue separate orders which can be priced and submitted in the monthly valuations and, therefore, not leave work unpriced over many months.

From the contractors' viewpoint, their involvement in measured term contracts can be restrictive in terms of maximising profit. As the contract is ostensibly based on the client's terms and conditions and a schedule of rates, there is little room for manoeuvre in attempting to increase the contractor's profit margin. Any excessive price additions to the tender will be easily seen by the client and the tender rejected. It is therefore, sometimes with reluctance that the contractor takes on a measured term contract commitment with its low profit potential. The other side of the coin, however, is when one considers the job security that the contractor has in accepting the contract. The contractor has a steady flow of work for a period of years, usually three, but in practice it may be more through extensions to the contract term given by a satisfied client. The contractor could be said to have the client as a captive audience over the period of the term, which allows a monopoly over the work as the concept inherently excludes all competitors.

Although the contractor must accept a lower profit margin than might be the case on other types of contract, it is a longer term and steady income without having the pressure and risk associated with other forms of contractual arrangement. It is not uncommon for a major general building contractor to be employed on such contracts over many years with their contracts being renewed, almost automatically, beyond the initial term of engagement. In difficult economic climates it is such contracts that enable contractors to maintain a regular income whilst gambling other finances in their more risky speculative ventures in the open construction market.

Daywork within measured term contracts

The measured term contract presupposes that all works orders issued by the client are for works which are quantifiable and, therefore, measurable. It is obvious that, from time to time situations will arise when the nature and scale of the work will be such that the contractor deems the work to be unmeasurable and applies to the client for daywork status. Indeed, there will be cases where the client feels the work is of such a difficult and messy nature, perhaps involving work in a restrictive area or in a hostile environment, that the work is more appropriately priced on a daywork basis. Usually, daywork rates would only be used in a measured term contract where the work is so dissimilar from the normal items of work that comparable and suitable rates cannot be found within the schedule upon which measurement can be based. The applicability of the daywork rate versus measured scheduled rates is an area of some ambiguity and an issue that is addressed subsequently in greater detail.

Tender evaluation

Measured Term Contracts are evaluated by the client on the basis of the percentage adjustment applied, by the tendering contractor, to the value of the works to be measured using the schedule of rates. If the tender requires the contractor to include one percentage adjustment only, then it is easy for the client to compare one tender with another. In such simple evaluations the tender specifying the lowest percentage addition to the schedule is usually selected. The tenders, like all quotations for work, should be carefully considered. This is achieved with the aid of a tender evaluation summary, an example of which is shown in Appendix 1. If the lowest tender is excessively low it may mean that the contractor is 'buying the work' at a loss, perhaps to stave off competition for the contract. This situation would not unduly worry the client if the contractor is reputable but there could be some cause for concern if the contractor's under-cutting policy resulted in the contractor being unable to fulfil the contractual obligations because of insolvency. As with all tendering situations, the client would tend to investigate extreme anomalies. Whereas experienced tenderers may submit a low bid quite deliberately, a new and possibly naive tenderer may submit a low tender through ignorance or error. It is always in the client's interest, and frequently in the contractor's interest also, to determine the true basis of the tender.

The tender may require more than a single percentage addition where, for example, the client procures the contract in work value bands, this being where the works orders are categorised into groups according to their values. Such contracts may necessitate the contractor adding a number of percentage adjustments corresponding to the work value bands. As before the client can easily confirm these percentage adjustments and make any necessary comparison. The client will wish to examine any figures specified by the tenderer relating to possible dayworks. To the client, it is essential that daywork is minimised, unless otherwise agreed, and kept within the schedule of rates, although it may be in the contractor's interest to include more works in a daywork category to minimise any potential risk. It is important to appreciate that although the client can compare the different tenders in terms of the percentage adjustments to the schedule, the client is not comparing the term contract final value. The tender is not a lump sum price as the works are unspecified, in fact, the volume of work is purely notional at the tendering stage.

The only guide to final cost is seen in the ECV or EAV which, if accurately anticipated by the client, is, at best, an approximation of the annual or final contract costs. Usually, the client will determine the ECV or EAV within a margin of five to ten per cent and always incorporates a contingency allowance to meet any unforeseen eventuality.

Tender evaluation, where involving an experienced tenderer, is normally a straightforward matter where the lowest tender is almost always selected. As mentioned previously, where there is a wide fluctuation in tender prices, investigation would automatically ensue. If the contractor is a new tenderer to measured term contracts then the contractor would certainly be consulted by the client to discuss the implications of any anomaly and to review the position of the tender.

Tender meetings

It is not uncommon for the client to hold pre-tender meetings with prospective tenderers, on an individual basis, to discuss the approach, method and implications of the tendering process. This will, obviously, be advantageous to a new tenderer. Such meetings are always conducted on an individual basis to ensure the tenderer's confidentiality. Similarly, it is often the case that the client will hold a pre-award meeting to review the successful tender itself. This is important, where, for example, a new and possibly naive tenderer has submitted a low bid in error, as it allows both parties the opportunity to discuss and rectify the tender or even to withdraw the tender without the tenderer losing face publicly.

Moreover, it can save greater embarrassment later should serious problems develop during the term of the contract. Such an eventuality might have catastrophic effects for both the client and the contractor in the construction marketplace. It is, generally, preferable to resolve the problems informally, amicably and confidentially. Formalities of this nature are carried out in practice, primarily to safeguard the interests of the client, but, also to protect the inexperienced contractor who may not fully appreciate the intricacies of his commitment.

Tender selection

A contractor may submit a tender with an extremely low, if any, element of profit included. In a poor economic climate a contractor may have to 'buy work' simply to maintain continuity of employment for his workforce, or more deviously to oust rival tenderers. The circumstances surrounding this will be of obvious interest to the client but may not be the main criteria upon which selection will be based. If the client is satisfied that the tender is sound, genuine and in good faith it will be accepted even with the low bid prevailing. What must be considered, however, is the more devious element that may lie behind low tendering strategy, where a low bid is deliberately targeted at undermining rival contractors and moreover, to unsettle an existing term contractor. Situations have occurred where a large contractor has gone into tender suffering a considerable financial loss but with the express intent to push out an existing contractor and also to gain a perceived foothold for future work. Although this situation is far from ever acknowledged it does happen, in particular, where a major contracting organisation is seeking to diversify or strategically expand into a new geographic location.

The difficulty for such a tenderer is that the sitting tenant, the current contractor, is in the best position to tender for the renewal of the term contract. The sitting contractor will already have the site set up, the organisation and the ongoing relationship with the client and, in practice, it is hard for a rival tenderer to undermine and dislodge this contractor. When the client is not entirely satisfied with the contractor however, the opportunity may present itself for a more unscrupulous tenderer. As the grapevine within construction is always informative it is not difficult for new tenderers to acquire advantageous information which may be beneficial in compiling their tender.

In practice, the client will only employ those contractors who are fully able to meet his needs. More often than not, a tender will be accepted not only on the percentage adjustment to the schedule but also be based upon the contractor's reputation. When the term contract comes up for re-tender, the sitting contractor, if highly thought of by the client, is likely to be given an extension to the contract. This is often preferred by clients who, would otherwise, have to embark upon the costly and involved process of re-letting the term contract.

Should the term contract invite new tenders, the sitting contractor remains in an advantageous position as sufficient time has elapsed for the contractor to appreciate the intricacies of the work, address any problems that may have arisen and submit a new tender that should be most competitive in the client's view.

The argument for measured term contracts

It is sometimes argued that there is little advantage in letting a contract on a measured term arrangement over procurement of work on a works order basis or even lump sum tendering. The greatest advantage lies in the fact that only one set of contract documents is needed, these being required for tendering purposes. If all the individual small works, instructed by works order under a term contract, were instead to be procured on a lump sum basis there would be a multitude of small and quite separate contracts each requiring their own contract documentation, drawings and specifications. This duplication and inefficiency is avoided with the term contract approach. On a works order basis, the outcome of the works cannot be anticipated before the contract, the estimated cost hardly accurate and there can be wide variations in eventual cost since there is considerable scope for the works to procrastinate and be overcharged by a malingering contractor.

Another crucial advantage of the measured term contract is that small works come under a much greater degree of management co-ordination and control than might be the case under other contractual arrangements. Because the works are formalised in terms of scheduling and budgetary control, it can be more effectively managed on a daily basis.

From the client's viewpoint, the relationship between the client and the contractor is much closer and this has undoubted benefits. On works procured using individual works orders, rather than under term contract, there is little compulsion for the contractor to carry out the work quickly, efficiently or effectively and there is a strong likelihood that overcharging will result. There is also little opportunity for retributive action against a contractor who maintains inadequate performance. The client is aware that the contractor is unlikely to return to the job to carry out remedial work and is more likely to forfeit retention monies if applicable and leave the work unfinished. This may necessitate the client engaging a new contractor to duly complete the works. On a term contract it is not likely that a contractor will leave a job unfinished given that he is employed by the client on a long-term basis. Better supervision, resources and management will ensure that adequate attention is given to fully completing the work required.

Administration

For the smaller building contractor, measured term contracts can pose a great many difficulties and problems in terms of their administration and these, in turn, can create difficulties for the client. Problems tend, in the main, to surround the aspects of site control, methods of measurement and co-ordination of different activities by a very small number of administrative staff. In small construction organisations, such responsibilities could, indeed, fall to one individual who must do everything from receiving and processing a works order to finalising the account for the works. This person is likely to have the necessary capability, experience and expertise to manage the technical aspects of executing the work but may have difficulty in the measurement activity. Such problems are, of course, alleviated in the larger building contractor where trades foremen and general foremen will manage the technical aspects whilst a quantity surveyor will handle the measurement and financial concerns.

In the same way that problems may arise for the contractor due to its organisational scale, so the client may suffer similar problems. With the client organisation, particularly if it too is small, one individual may be assigned to undertake all aspects from issuing the works orders to agreeing the final account.

The primary concerns of the small contractor lie not so much in the difficulties of understanding or undertaking the individual tasks themselves but in the multiplicity of activities that must be accomplished at the same time. It is simply not possible to procure the many works orders, monitor the works adequately, measure the works and compile and finalise valuations simultaneously. For this reason alone, it is sensible for the small contractor to isolate the mechanisms of the technical and managerial aspects from the measurement and financial aspects.

The management of small works under a measured term contract is of a highly specialised nature, a fact that is frequently ignored, or underestimated. The success of a measured term contract, as with any other contractual arrangement, is heavily dependent upon the effectiveness of its management. Frequently, term contracts are regarded by the larger contractor as forgotten cousins, important in their ability to maintain workload and labour continuity, but of little interest because of their propensity towards low profit margins. In addition, it is not uncommon to find that contractors appoint their most solid and reliable, but less dynamic staff on term contracts. This is understandable given that the contracts are not themselves excessively dynamic in nature, but disappointing in that measured term contracts do need, like all projects, positive and creative attitudes in management if the best results are to be achieved. Such contracts are often used as a vehicle for the development of staff in so much that they provide a stable, low risk environment in which younger personnel can be trained. Again one might seriously question such an attitude and approach, because to the client, measured term contracts are often a major commitment and are of no lesser significance than new build construction projects. They should therefore be treated by the contractor with the same regard.

The organisation by clients for term contracts can take many forms but usually follow a general approach. Major clients, for example in the manufacturing, engineering, petrochemical and similar large capital intensive industries, will, through their own internal organisation, be structured into work sections or production plants each with their own building administrative officer, usually denoted as a Works Superintendent, Supervising Officer or Works Engineer. This 'superintendent' will oversee all building work within the designated section. If the section is sufficiently large, the superintendent is likely to be assisted by one or more subordinates, (Works Foremen), to oversee the day-to-day site activities. The superintendent and assistants will be responsible to the client organisation for issuing orders and, instructions, liaising with the contractor, initiating and monitoring the works and ensuring that the works undertaken meet with the expectations, specifications and conditions of the schedule and form of contract.

The measurement aspects of the contract will be managed by a quantity surveyor who might be an in-house employee or a member of a private quantity surveying practice. The client's quantity surveyor will oversee all financial activities, including development of the schedule of rates, assessing tender bids, liaising with the selected contractor, measuring and checking the work on site, verifying the contractor's interim valuations and compiling the final account. Smaller clients are likely to appoint a technically oriented person to fulfil the role of the superintendent and, in addition, employ a quantity surveyor, brought in from outside the organisation on a fee basis, to avoid a permanent organisational overhead. It can be seen in both cases, that the client should generally try to separate the technical aspect from the financial aspect of management.

On the contractor's side, the contract is likely to be managed and run just like any other project. Contract organisation will take the same basic hierarchical framework as other building projects. This will involve a contracts manager or site agent, ably assisted by general and trades foremen, an engineer and site personnel on the technical side with a contractor's quantity surveyor to assume financial management. The working relationship between the client and contractor will primarily involve the client's superintendent liaising closely with the contractor's contracts manager or agent as the primary flow of instructions, (works orders), and feedback channels will be between these individuals. Similarly, from the financial viewpoint, the client's quantity surveyor will liaise with the contractor's quantity surveyor in the usual way.

The main difference between the term contract arrangement and a 'traditional' building contract is the absence of the design consultant or architect. The design element is subsumed within the client's organisation with the works superintendent and assistants designing and specifying basic works themselves or referring the work to a design drawing office whose function it is to detail the works and produce the specifications. Cost estimates for the work will be undertaken by the client's quantity surveyor in liaison with the design office. A typical contract organisation for small works measured term contracts is illustrated in Figure 4.1.

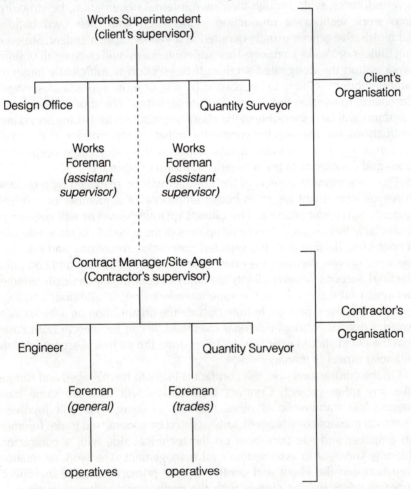

Figure 4.1 Organisation for medium/large measured term contract

Work on site

The issue of the client's instructions, (works orders), to the contractor should be undertaken directly by the client's supervisor, the works superintendent, and issued directly to the contractor's contract manager or site agent. This direct single line of communication, authority and feedback has distinct advantages for both parties. With this formalised and well designated approach, there is less opportunity for the communications to be interrupted, corrupted or misperceived. All instructions for work should be placed by means of a works order, (sometimes referred to as a 'Foreman's Order'), issued by the superintendent. Duplicate copies should be filed for record purposes, issued to the client's works foreman, and to the client's quantity surveyor for costing purposes. In practice, given the administration complexities of some measured term contracts, the superintendent will delegate power to issue orders to the works foreman.

When the works order is received by the contractor's supervisor the original will be retained for record purposes and copies passed to the appropriate foreman to process the works and to the quantity surveyor for valuation purposes. Work is progressed on the site by the contractor to the drawings and specifications provided by the client on the order, together with other associated written and verbal information that may be given. See example of standard forms presented in Appendix 1. The work is monitored on site by the contracts manager and foreman in liaison with the client's works superintendent and foreman. As works are completed or partially completed within the monthly valuation period the works are measured and priced by the contractor's quantity surveyor to the schedule of rates. When all works for the period are priced the interim valuation is compiled and presented to the client's quantity surveyor for valuation and agreement. The prominent features of the process are shown in Figure 4.2.

Whilst the vast majority of small works present little difficulty to either the client or contractor, there are a number of issues to consider. The works superintendent, or the works foreman, should maintain an active presence on site throughout the works. They should conduct site checks, where necessary, particularly on those orders for work where the nature differs from routine orders or one in which higher costs are anticipated. The benefit of close supervision is to, firstly maintain a general presence on the site and, secondly to demonstrate clearly that works orders are not issued blindly and that checks will take place. It is useful for the client's quantity surveyor to maintain a similar profile to show unequivocally that measurement and cost validation is also being conducted. Even where, for example on high cost orders, the quantity surveyor has maintained a strong presence at the workplace, it is still good practice to physically measure and check the contractor's quantity surveying functions.

It is also advantageous for the client if the superintendent personally

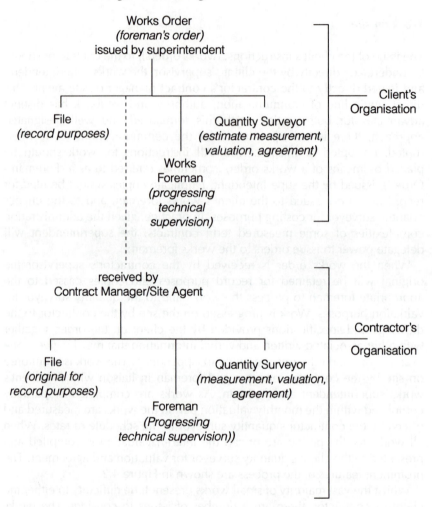

Works Order
(foreman's order)
issued by superintendent

Client's
Organisation

File
(record purposes)

Quantity Surveyor
*(estimate measurement,
valuation, agreement)*

Works
Foreman
*(progressing
technical
supervision)*

received by
Contract Manager/Site Agent

Contractor's
Organisation

File
*(original for
record purposes)*

Quantity Surveyor
*(measurement, valuation,
agreement)*

Foreman
*(Progressing
technical supervision))*

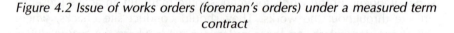

*Figure 4.2 Issue of works orders (foreman's orders) under a measured term
contract*

makes regular site checks, since the superintendent will have both written
and issued the order and given instructions based upon that order. It is,
therefore, prudent for the superintendent to assess the effectiveness of his
own decisions and judgements. Any amendments or alterations to the
original works order, although likely to be given verbally, should always be
confirmed in writing with copies to all concerned. The variation should also
specify the anticipated cost increase, or reduction, to aid the task of the
quantity surveyor in verifying the valuation for the work. Once more, regular
checks on site are essential to elucidate any perceived differences between

the anticipated cost and the valued measure submitted by the contractor's quantity surveyor.

Measurement

The estimated price of a works order will be anticipated by the client's works superintendent from experience and historic records, or provided by the quantity surveyor from pre-measuring the work and pricing from the schedule of rates. The estimate, in practice, will be a reasonably accurate assessment of the value of the major aspects of the work plus a percentage allowance to cover the cost of the remaining minor items. It is essential that such an estimate has close accuracy, as an under-estimate could lead to unexpected rises on expenditure when the valuation and final account are submitted. Over-estimating can, equally, become a problem to the future budgeting aspects of the contract.

The contractor's quantity surveyor will measure both the finalised and ongoing works orders and form the basis for an interim valuation to be submitted to the client, normally at monthly intervals. Standard forms are shown in Appendix 1. Measurement of the works conducted on site will be undertaken by the quantity surveyor who monitors and measures the work as it proceeds and subsequently when it is completed. Information will also be acquired from the foreman supervising the particular works order. In practice, where for example the work reverts to an agreed daywork basis, the record of manhours, plant and materials used will be recorded and provided by the foreman concerned. The quantity surveyor will price up these submissions and submit this claim along with the measured works in an appropriate valuation.

When works orders have been fully completed within the month, i.e. during the interim period, these are measured and priced in accordance with the schedule of rates and their final value is then calculated. Where only a part of the work is complete at the time of the interim valuation, the quantity surveyor may measure the work in one of two ways. He may measure the part of the work completed, or by claiming the proportion of the full estimated cost equating to the proportion of the work thought to be complete. Alternatively, as mentioned previously, the work may not be measured until final completion. The contractor should try to avoid this approach since outstanding payments can obviously lead to cash flow problems, particularly with small contractors.

On larger measured term contracts, the client's quantity surveyor will treat the contractor's interim valuation as an accurate and detailed cost assessment for the month's work. He will liaise closely with the contractor's quantity surveyor, arrange to measure or spot check on site some of the works orders to verify the contractor's measurements and claim for the interim valuation. Both surveyors will attend a monthly site financial meeting to review the interim valuation and agree the sum due for interim payment.

On smaller term contracts it may be uneconomic for the client to employ a quantity surveyor on a full time basis. A slightly different approach may, therefore, be adopted. The client's small works supervisor should be sufficiently competent to measure the work and to make an assessment of the cost incurred based upon the original estimates. Financial management of this type may be used by the client throughout the contract term and only when the annual account is due will a quantity surveyor be employed to prepare and administer this. An alternative approach may see the interim valuations complied without the work being measured in detail. In this case, the interim valuation will be subject to re-measurement in the annual or final term account. Finalising measurement is an important aspect. The client's and contractor's quantity surveyor respectively will liaise, discuss and determine, quite clearly, whether the works measured are finalised as the contract proceeds or are subject to re-measurement.

Payment for the work covered by an individual order is settled by means of a final account for that individual order. Once the work is completed, measured, finalised and agreed, there should be no need to address the order thereafter. The annual value of the contract is the agreed cost of all the works completed within the year and the total term contract value is the cost of all the works orders raised during the contract term. While these values can only be anticipated before the term begins, the actual values in the contract should always be checked and assessed against the cost plan to ensure that budgetary control is actively invoked. This should be employed as an ongoing activity and not a task undertaken retrospectively at the conclusion of the contract term.

With the vast majority of works orders, the work is completed, measured and account submitted within a relatively short time period, (*between one to three months*). Problems can arise if the work becomes prolonged for any reason. When this occurs there are implications to the measurement, not least of which is the efficiency of the updating term contract price adjustment figures. The adjustment percentage, as applied, is directly related to the date when the work order was raised and not to the date when the work is carried out. If the work is prolonged for many months and increases occur in the cost of resources during the period when the works order is open, the increases will have to be borne by the contractor and not by the client. Rather than leave orders open where work is not progressing, the contractor will request that the client close the order in writing to suspend the work and issue a new order at an appropriate time. Alternatively, the contractor may seek more preferential daywork rates where, perhaps, it is felt that there is an opportunity for greater reimbursement.

It is normal for the interim valuation to claim payment for the 'full' value of the works order. Retention money is not usually a feature of measured term contracts. There would be little merit in the client retaining money, because the retention value would be small, but moreover, the contractor will be remaining on the contract for the term and consequently there should be little difficulty for the client in getting the contractor to rectify any inadequate works.

Whilst there are usually few problems to confront the surveyors in financially managing a term contract, the arrangement can leave advantageous doors open to the more enterprising or unscrupulous contractor's quantity surveyor, against which the client must invoke safeguards. Typical problems ostensibly surround the level of vigilance paid by the client's works superintendent and client's quantity surveyor to the day-to-day technical and financial management of the works.

On smaller term contracts where the client does not employ a quantity surveyor on a continual basis it is easy to become somewhat reliant upon the diligence and honesty of the contractor's quantity surveyor in measuring and submitting the valued account for the works. Occasional checks may not identify over-measurement or claims for items of work which have not really been undertaken. The client must ensure that a system of management is adopted that gives due care and attention to close liaison between the two parties. Ideally, the measurement of the works should be a collaborative exercise regularly undertaken but with independent spot checks by the client or his representative to verify exact measurement and valuation.

Even on larger term contracts where the client employs a quantity surveyor there can be a tendency for the client's surveyor to become complacent and be too reliant upon the efforts of the contractor's quantity surveyor. It is common practice on term contracts for the contractor's quantity surveyor to undertake measurement and valuation in isolation from the client's quantity surveyor, save for the monthly interim valuation meeting. The contractor's quantity surveyor will prepare an interim valuation based on work orders priced on measured rates from the schedule, or *pro rata* the work if not finalised. The summary does not present the breakdown of measurement or cost which is calculated on the dimensions sheets and abstracts (*surveyors measurement and calculation sheets*), these being retained and filed by the contractor's quantity surveyor. Only the summary page forms part of the monthly valuation. The summary presents little more than a list of the works order numbers and their price. If for example, the measured value of the order is checked by the client's quantity surveyor against the estimate of cost and is lower or comparable it will usually be accepted by the client despite the fact that the detailed calculations have not been scrutinised. The client's quantity surveyor should always expect to review the contractor's calculation sheets in arriving at the value for the works order.

It is also advisable to spot check the measurements and calculations independently from the contractor's surveyor to ensure that accurate costings have been submitted. Whilst it should not be inferred that the contractor's quantity surveyor will claim for work that the contractor has not really undertaken, the general approach will be to err on the side of caution in their valuations. The contractor's surveyor will tend to raise the price by measuring generously and rounding-up calculations. Whilst such effects will be minor on individual orders due to the nature of small works themselves, the effects when multiplied over a great many works orders could be considerable. It is this full value effect which must be appreciated by the client's quantity surveyor.

It is also possible that through ignorance, error or opportunity that inappropriate rates from the schedule may have been used to price the works. Schedules of rates can contain hundreds of individually calculated rates and it is quite easy for the contractor's quantity surveyor to use the wrong rate or deliberately apply a more favourable rate. Again, while it might not be possible or be really feasible for the client's quantity surveyor to identify where the inappropriate rate may have been used, only careful diligence and effort will identify the problem. For the quantity surveyors involved, negotiating the interim valuations, deliberating over the rates used and justifying their measurement approach are the interesting and intriguing aspects of term contract quantity surveying. It is commonplace for the contractor's quantity surveyor to attempt to claim a more favourable rate for an item of work while the client's quantity surveyor will argue for a lesser, more appropriate rate.

For example, considerable debate may surround the definition of what constitutes a stanchion base or a plinth. Whilst the difference may be minimal aesthetically, the sequence and volume of construction operations may be measured differently based on the schedule of rates. Where ambiguity arises the surveyors will invariably discuss and compromise with an intermediate rate agreed to the satisfaction of both parties. In most cases, the acceptance is based upon the client's quantity surveyor feeling that something has been saved and the contractor's surveyor feeling something has been gained. As long as one party is not feeling cheated a sense of fairness will prevail.

It is also quite feasible for items to be measured, priced and inserted in the valuation when, they had not been used in the works. For example, the contractor's quantity surveyor may measure timbering to the sides of trench excavations when timbering was not involved. Again, this anomaly could be genuine if the contractor's quantity surveyor had not seen the job, or alternatively it could be a deliberate inclusion to increase the measured cost. If the client had not seen the work on site and witnessed the use of timbering, the client would not be in an appropriate position to argue against its inclusion in the valuation. Although this is another isolated incident with minimal significant effect, the combined effect of over-measurement across many individual jobs could be considerable.

All the aforementioned problems can be attributed to inadequate financial management of the term contract. Resolution of the difficulties is heavily reliant upon the dedication of the client's quantity surveyor and the honesty and integrity of the contractor's quantity surveyor. In practice, over the course of several years a working relationship will build up between the surveying parties such that measurement and the agreement of accounts will be undertaken in an amicable and collaborative way, with the foibles of each being well known to the other. It is really a case of balancing the various levels of professional trust and suspicion between the parties to reach a happy working medium.

In terms of day-to-day working practice, each valuation submitted should specify the works order number, summary of cost, a breakdown of the calculations, be measured on site by both parties and agreed with reference to the schedule of rates. In this way, each individual works order will receive the level of attention it needs to be efficiently and effectively managed. The necessary procedures for potential success in managing small works under a measured term contract is shown in Figure 4.3.

The contractor may, when pricing a works order, seek to specify all the work or part of the work on a daywork basis. This occurs where it is felt that the schedule of rates does not cover the precise work content and the contractor does not wish to risk being out of pocket through any inadequacies in the schedule. Indeed, when the schedule does not provide a suitable rate to measure the works, an alternative should be sought. This could entail a renegotiation of the price basis in favour of daywork status, or more likely involve measurement based on similar rates taken from the schedule. As there will be many rates contained in a typical schedule there will undoubtedly be similar and suitable rates upon which to prepare measurement. Only where no rates are found to be appropriate should the daywork status be granted.

To prevent argument over measurement concepts all work, where to be measured on a daywork basis, should be agreed in advance of it being carried out. It is sensible not to mix scheduled rates and daywork on any order, although the contractor may seek to combine the two forms of measurement in the valuations. Only in extreme circumstances should the client ever accept this and should normally ask the contractor to measure the work on similar rates from the schedule of rates and refrain from using daywork rates unless authorised on a separate daywork order.

The advantages of the measured term contract

Advantages
When the client is seeking to procure many small works, there are many distinct advantages. These can be summarised as follows:

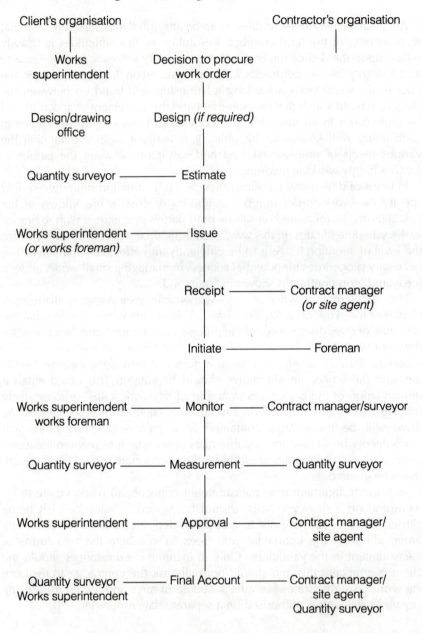

Client's organisation   Contractor's organisation

Works superintendent   Decision to procure work order

Design/drawing office   Design *(if required)*

Quantity surveyor ———— Estimate

Works superintendent ———— Issue
(or works foreman)

Receipt ———— Contract manager
(or site agent)

Initiate ———— Foreman

Works superintendent ———— Monitor ———— Contract manager/surveyor
works foreman

Quantity surveyor ———— Measurement ———— Quantity surveyor

Works superintendent ———— Approval ———— Contract manager/
site agent

Quantity surveyor ———— Final Account ———— Contract manager/
Works superintendent   site agent
                                               Quantity surveyor

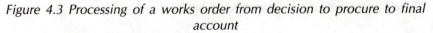

Figure 4.3 Processing of a works order from decision to procure to final account

- Simple approach to formalising the procurement of multiple small works which would otherwise have to be undertaken under individual jobbing works orders or, for larger works, carried out under a small lump sum fixed price contract.
- Relatively simple form of contract with little documentation.
- Simple measurement and valuation using a schedule of rates.
- Contract can be non-competitive or competitive by tendering.
- Tender analysis is simplified by assessing the various percentage adjustments, added by the tenderer, to the basic schedule of rates.
- Widely understood and accepted method for procuring small works, whether they be maintenance and repair or minor capital projects.
- Contract organisation is straightforward, yet retains sufficient flexibility for both small operations and larger, more complex works.
- Use of Estimated Contract Value, (ECV), or Estimated Annual Value, (EAV), means budgetary control is available to the client.
- All instructions given by the client, including variations to works are issued in written form, (*Works orders or Foreman's Orders*), presenting fewer difficulties through poor communication.
- Work continuity is heightened as the contractor is employed over a contract term rather than engaged on a stop-start basis.
- Ample opportunity for the client and contractor's site organisation to interrelate and build up useful liaison, teamwork and trust during the contract term.
- Approach is economic, given work continuity and economies of scale make individual small works cheaper than if they are procured in isolation.
- The lead-in time for individual small works is faster and work duration shorter than if they are procured in isolation.

Disadvantages
Despite the many, seemingly obvious, advantages of using a measured term contract, its approach can present some difficulties and problems. The main disadvantages are:

- Although the Estimated Contract Value, (ECV), or Estimate Annual Value, (EAV), can give an approximate cost profile, the contract remains subject to variable cost.
- Successful administration relies heavily upon the contractor's diligence, care and commitment to 'routine', more so than in other contracts, and such factors as methodic ordering, monitoring, measurement and valuation are paramount.
- System is firmly dependent upon the honesty and integrity of the contractor, in particular in site measurement and valuation. Opportunity may exist for the enterprising or unscrupulous contractor to take advantage of the client.

- While the measured term contract is undoubtedly successful, mainly due to the development of a close relationship between that client and contractor, there is a possibility, in the long-term, that the professional separation of the parties may give way to a 'cosy' working relationship which makes the parties complacent in their respective roles and functions.
- If for any reason the contractor is changed there will be difficulty in maintaining continuity and a high likelihood of work being left unfinished.

4.4   Daywork term contract

Definition

Where the characteristics of small works are such that they do not readily facilitate accurate description, detailed construction method and unambiguous measurement, an alternative form of contract arrangement may be sought. Similarly, where the volume of work may be such that it would not be feasible to procure each small work job separately on an individual lump sum basis, so an alternative form of contract may be more appropriate. In such situations, the use of a *Daywork Term Contract* may be favoured. With a daywork term contract the client, instead of issuing a series of separate daywork orders to individual contractors, procures a daywork contract for a set term under which one selected contractor carries out the series of small works on a daywork payment basis. In essence, the daywork term contract follows closely the pattern of the measured term contract with the difference being in the basis of payment. A daywork term contract can be let on a noncompetitive basis or be competitive. The basis of the contract is that payment for the work undertaken is founded upon the actual number of construction operatives employed and the manhours expended by each in fulfilling the task, together with reimbursement for the plant and materials used (hence the term Cost Reimbursement Contract). Overheads and profit are added to the nett resources used to arrive at the full cost of the works. Were individual lump sum contracts to be used for each individual small work item rather than a daywork term approach, the cost implication would be excessive and therein lies the main virtue of the daywork term contract. It is a most economic method of procuring an ongoing series of unspecified works.

Pricing policy

When a daywork term contract is let competitively, the client awards the contract on the basis of the different percentage adjustments to the basic daywork rates by each tenderer. The basic daywork rates for trades and general operatives are specified by wage councils and agreed by unions and employers so these can be regarded as fixed rates. The tenderer adds to these rates a percentage adjustment to cover for all organisational overheads, both on and off site, and finally adds the designated profit level.

Other additional costs forming part of the percentage adjustment will include transportation costs for plant items, such as vehicles dispatched from a head office plant depot, haulage for materials such as the removal of surplus spoil to tips, and the like. Should the work necessitate the employment of sub-contractors then the appropriate rates to be charged by the sub-contractor should be specified and allowances made for any taxes applicable. The client's choice of tender is made relatively simple, since only the percentage adjustments included by the contractor need to be reviewed as the basis of the payment, the wage rates, are fixed among the different tenderers.

The tenderer for daywork contracts, like those for measured term contracts, needs complete information upon which to determine the percentage adjustment. The contractor's tender documents will, therefore, specify: the ECV or EAV for the works; the location; dispersion; nature and detail of the anticipated workplaces; and specification for the works. The duration of a daywork term contract is usually three years and may include an option to terminate the arrangement at the end of any given year should the client be dissatisfied with the contractor's performance. It is more than coincidence that daywork term contracts and measured term contracts run for the same length of duration. Quite often, major clients will let both types of contract concurrently and sometimes even to the same contractor. The contract could be let completely separately or jointly as a daywork maintenance and minor capital project. The contract may be arranged on a competitive basis or by contractor selection; in fact, many permutations exist for the client when procuring the works.

Administration of daywork term contract

Continuity of work

The main benefit of the daywork term contract for the client is that the discontinuity and associated difficulties of letting many small lump sum contracts, the alternative approach, is removed. For the contractor, there is undoubted benefit that work is assured for the term of the contract and a strong likelihood that further terms will be granted if the contractor's level of performance is acceptable to the client. There is also a genuine cost advantage to the client in procuring all the works through the one contract, as it alleviates the repetitive cost of preparing separate contract documents for each individual small work item. In addition, the contractor should achieve greater efficiency and economies of scale through the continuity of operations.

Performance
The client is virtually assured that the contractor will provide a reasonable and acceptable level of performance. Although the performance and quality of work can never be guaranteed, the daywork term contract, like the measured term form, reaps the benefit of employing the contractor on a prolonged basis. It is therefore, quite easy for the client to initiate remedial action if the works are not carried out to the requisite standard. As the contractor is always going to be present on the site of the works there is a much greater likelihood that the work will be duly completed to standard and at the first attempt. This is likely to be even more so, given that the contractor is being paid on a time related basis. There is simply no need for the contractor to hurry the work and cut corners.

The fact that the contractor feels little compulsion to hurry the work does, of course, have one distinct implication in that the work may become procrastinated as speed is not of the essence unless other work pressures are bearing. The contractor should, as far as possible, ensure that a realistic time is taken to complete the work, neither lengthened nor rushed excessively. There can be a tendency for operatives to linger over work as there is no motivation to hasten progress dramatically as financial reward is the set daywork rate plus bonus, the bonus itself usually being based on a standardised rate rather than being performance based. This can be alleviated by the contractor using a performance related cost and bonus scheme, although it is well recognised within the industry that bonuses on daywork term contracts are nowhere near as lucrative as other construction projects. The work nature itself does not tend to afford an opportunity to make bonus since there is little continuity of task and only small volumes of work to undertake, General awareness of such characteristics mean that daywork, therefore, does not tend to attract the more dynamic and go-ahead bonus seeking operative, but rather employs the steady and methodic type of person.

On large engineering plants which, for example, a contractor may have one daywork term contract amongst a number of other large, traditionally procured construction projects, there can be a general feeling among the workers that the term contract, while providing continuity of work over a longer period, presents little opportunity for financial incentive and career development. This can frequently give rise to resentment between the operatives on the different sites, in particular where there is transfer of labour, across sites to meet short term changes in work demands.

Supervision and management

Because of the possible dispersed location and nature of small works, it is frequently difficult for the client to maintain adequate checking procedures on the contractor's workforce when they are assigned to, what are essentially, unsupervised sites. Similarly, it is difficult for the contractor to maintain detailed supervision on a constant basis and this problem can exist even on a well defined term contract site. In practice, the labour force will simply have to be trusted to carry out the work effectively and efficiently and at their own discretion.

Periodic checks are nevertheless to be conducted to verify the general working practices. Such spot checks can be used to approve final accounts for each daywork order valuation. When the contractor submits the account, each daywork order should: record the order number; list the name and trade of the operatives employed on the work; and detail the hours spent each day on the job.

The client may even ask to see the contractor's labour returns from the foreman to verify the working time as the operatives may be working slowly, lingering deliberately or simply not working at all. The client must, therefore, approve only what is deemed to be an acceptable duration for the work based on judgement and approve an acceptable level of manhours expended. The client will always have a notional assessment of the realistic hours taking into account productive, indirectly productive and non-productive work elements. It is easy to see, however, that the contractor could take advantage of the client in the valuation submission, particularly if supervision is lacking. Again, the practical situation relies heavily upon the integrity and honesty of the contractor and the trust placed in the contractor by the client.

When the daywork term contract is used, say in a large engineering plant situation, the client has reasonable opportunity to monitor the contractor, yet discrepancies often occur because the client does not take the opportunity to supervise proficiently. Some work tasks, however, involve the contractor sending a small workforce to quite distant and remote locations away from the watchful eye of the client. These, in many ways can be the most expensive small works undertaken on a daywork term basis since site supervision and control will be virtually non-existent and it takes particularly diligent and reliable operatives to complete the work realistically and efficiently. Extra cost will always be incurred in travelling time, transportation and the like, and allowances should always be made for slower working.

Where such occurrences are frequent, the contractor may choose to set up a mobile workshop to meet the requirements for small works on a travelling basis. This is common, for example in housebuilding where an after sales remedial service is provided by a mobile operative, directed and supplied by a regional office. Works from the mobile workshop are procured by a daywork order issued from the unit's supervisor at the regional office. An advantage of the approach is that the operatives are specialised in the work, travelling time and transportation is reduced and there can be a measure of call out for urgent works. Many clients have a high requirement for call out facilities, not necessary for new small works, but certainly for repairs and maintenance. There will be an obvious increase in initial organisation overheads in setting up a mobile workshop but this will be offset by the reduction in transport and travelling from office to workplace if each work task is procured individually.

In the same way that the measured term contract is frequently under-estimated, so too is the daywork term contract. To the contractor, its level of importance is understated although many realise that it provides, what amounts to, their bread and butter income. To the client, the daywork term contract provides an arrangement that is both effective and economically sound. Again, the success of the daywork term contract is firmly dependent upon the contractor taking the contract very seriously and managing the works diligently and reliably. Accomplishment comes down to the degree of liaison and co-operation between the term parties to make the daywork term contract work on a daily basis as the day-to-day management practices are paramount to success.

The advantages of the daywork term contract

The daywork term contract, along with any form of contractual arrange-ment, has both positive and negative aspects. The advantages and disad-vantages can be listed as follows:

Advantages

- May be used where a term contract is advantageous and desirable but where the type and nature of the work does not facilitate accurate description and measurement.
- The 'term' of the contract allows continuity of work pattern, both for the client and contractor.
- Term approach allows approximate budgeting to be undertaken to control work costs and the cash flow situation.
- Contract may be let on a competitive or non-competitive basis.
- Allows the contractor to cover costs of labour and plant on an hourly basis plus materials costs.
- Attractive method of procurement to a contractor where jobs are distant and remote and might be the only basis on which a client may engage the contractor.
- Tendering and administration are relatively easy for the client.
- Gives distinct cost advantage to the client rather than procuring each job separately on a daywork order basis or lump sum contract.
- Client is assured of contractor's quality and performance, since future work depends upon satisfaction of the client.

Disadvantages
- Contract can be difficult for the client to supervise, in particular where the work is remote.
- Arrangement is based upon the honesty and integrity of the contractor and the reliance that is placed upon the contractor to accurately record the manhours expended, and plant and materials used.
- Approach is subject to time and cost excesses where inadequate supervision and management is apparent.

Perhaps the most pertinent issue in the use of the daywork term contract is for the client to maintain a steady and even flow of daywork orders over the period of the contract. This is vital in not over-pressuring the contractor at any given point in time. Daywork orders should, therefore, follow an anticipated schedule of issue. In a situation where pressure exists the contractor may become over-stretched and is then prone to cut corners to keep up with progress and work quality is likely to suffer dramatically. Where daywork term contracts are arranged effectively, they can lead to undoubted economic benefits being accrued by the more discerning client and usually prove to be a stable and cost effective mode of employment for the contractor.

4.5 Annual term contract

Definition

The client may let both measured term and daywork term contracts with any contract duration although the most usual period of term is three years. A three year duration is the term recognised by most clients as giving the optimum contract performance in terms of efficiency, effectiveness and economy. There are instances, however, where the type, nature and volume of the expected works make contracts of three years unsuitable and, in such cases, an *Annual Term Contract* may be favoured. The annual term contract, by definition, lasts one year although it may renewed for further terms if circumstances permit. Whereas a measured term contract is based upon a broad range of work, of differing scale and type and employing a great diversity in trades, the annual term contract tends to be used where one trade or a single specialism predominates in the works. Such a situation can prevail in, for example, the erection and dismantling of scaffolding works, floor or wall finishes and specialised tiling, and the like. Many larger client organisations procure a general contractor on a three year measured term contract and, in addition, employ a specialised scaffolding contractor on an annual term contract which would be renewable over the three year period to run alongside the measured term contract. Frequently, the annual term contract is referred to, in practice, by the title of 'single trade term contract' which, perhaps, more accurately describes its true nature. The payment basis of the annual term contract may be one of measured or daywork terms depending upon the nature of the work, although its use is normally associated with payment on a measured schedule of rates basis. Where the contract was on a daywork basis, the contract would virtually be a daywork term contract with a one year duration.

Specialised schedule of rates

The annual term contract, due to the specialist nature of the contractor's work, cannot be structured around the general schedule of rates, but rather must be developed around a single trade schedule. Many larger clients who employ one trade regularly will develop their own single trade schedule of rates. When the client develops a single trade schedule, the content and detail of the document is limited to the precise nature of the specialist work and, therefore, it is much more accurate than if, say, one was to abstract a similar section from a general schedule. The single trade approach is nearly always linked to the annual term contract and this gives the client flexibility to procure special services over a prolonged period. In addition to promoting continuity, it allows the contract to be terminated quickly and efficiently should the work patterns change.

Again, the contract is favourable to the contractor as it provides a fixed surety of work, but, is obviously not as advantageous as the continuity of employment provided by the three year measured term contract. For this reason, many specialist contractors servicing larger clients, will procure a longer-term contract which is equivalent to that given to the general contractor under a measured term arrangement. The client will, in fact, often employ all the contractors, both the general contractor and the specialist, on the same term basis, whether it be an annual term contract or measured term contract simply to avoid the dissatisfaction created by disparity between the contractors, term and basis of employment.

Handling of tenders

The method by which an annual term contract is procured by the client is basically the same as for both the measured and daywork term contracts although the specialised nature of the single trade approach may give rise to some difficulty. The most noticeable issue surrounds the assessment of the tenders received by the client. Where a general contractor submits a tender for a measured term contract the tender is based on a general schedule of rates or one developed by the client. In either case, the client should be sufficiently familiar with the work to appreciate the percentage adjustments inserted by the contractor. With the single trade schedule, the work is likely to be specialised and, therefore, may be outside the experience and knowledge of the client. This will mean that the client may be unable to discern between the percentage adjustments inserted by the various tenderers. The client may not be able to verify the accuracy of the calculations nor decide which tender will best serve the needs of the contract. Only where quantities were included, which they are not, could the client glean any breakdown of the tender calculations. Like the measured term contract, the client will only provide an ECV or EAV and not have at his disposal precise details of the extent and volume of the work when letting the contract out to tender.

The contractor bases the tender on a percentage, as previously discussed under both the measured and daywork term approaches, and it is here that adjustments may appear higher than in the case of the general schedule of rates. This can be explained, since the work nature is more specialised and, therefore, higher overheads and more ancillary costs may be added and these will alter the percentage adjustment. In addition, the number of items in the schedule will be fewer and this affords less room for manoeuvre in measurement. To combat this lack of flexibility the contractor will increase the percentage adjustment to compensate.

Benefits

Overall, in the same way that there are cost benefits to adopting a measured term contract or a daywork term contract, the annual term contract is more cost effective to the client due to the economies of scale over the longer contract period than if the small works were procured singly by means of works orders. This particular aspect is most advantageous when considered against the alternative of having to procure many small and specialist contractors through individual lump sum contracts. Such an approach would greatly increase the client's overheads and, therefore, the annual term contract is a simple form of arrangement which alleviates the concern and reduces procurement cost.

4.6 Small/minor building work lump sum contract

Definitions

Despite the many variations of traditional and non-traditional forms of building procurement for large construction projects and available alternatives in term contract approach for regular small works, there will always be jobs which, in terms of their characteristics, fall between the two, too small for procurement on a major project basis and too large to justify the works order or jobbing approach. With the *Small/minor Lump Sum Contract,* the client lets the contract on a fixed price competitive basis. A number of the shorter forms of building contract are directly applicable to fixed price lump sum contracts. These are reviewed in the following chapter. The main differences between the small/minor lump sum contract and the other arrangements for procuring small works are illustrated in Figure 4.4.

It was previously mentioned that the main drawback of the lump sum fixed price contract is that it involves the client in excessive compilation of tender documents, preparation of drawings and detailed specifications, which all inflict a considerable cost burden on the organisation. It is often these implications alone that dissuades a client from using a lump sum contractual approach.

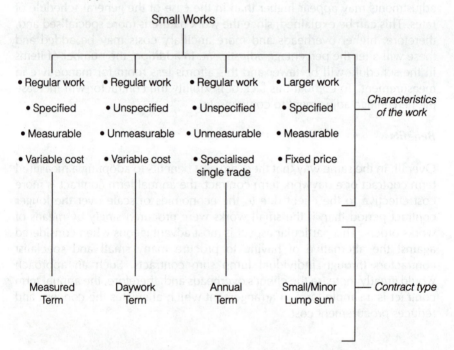

Figure 4.4 Differences between small/minor lump sum contract and other procurement arrangements

Type and volume of work

To be feasible, the work must be of sufficient technological complexity or volume that the work simply cannot be undertaken on an individual works order basis or a term contract. The client must decide carefully at what point the work exceeds the characteristics favourable to a works order or term arrangement. Lump sum fixed price contracts can have the benefit of being competitive or selective in tendering should the client so desire. Although clients should be encouraged to use open tendering to obtain the best possible choice of alternative contractors, lump sum contracts are often procured by selection. Moreover, the contractor who currently serves the client on a works order basis or term contract is in an advantageous position to win any lump sum tender. Such contractors have a distinct advantage in that they will already have an established relationship with the client, have the adminstration in place and, therefore, can undercut their rival tenderers. Where a project is sufficiently large to justify an individual lump sum approach, the project should, from the client's viewpoint, be kept completely separate from any ongoing works orders or term contracts.

On large engineering or petrochemical sites where a contractor might tender for a lump sum project whilst currently undertaking a term contract, difficulties can arise from confusing the two, as the project objectives can be different in each case. The two contracts should be treated separately, with different project organisation and adminstration for both the client and contractor.

Tendering

Tenders are based on detailed drawings and specifications provided by the client, upon which the contractor provides a contract sum for which the whole of the works will be carried out. It is, therefore, fundamental that the detail provided by the client is both accurate and full. Any omissions in the documentation will result in errors in the price which will require variation orders to rectify during the contract period. Any errors of detail in the documentation, drawings or specifications will affect all the prices received from the tenderers, so full and careful information is a prerequisite to its use and success.

Tender evaluation

Being a lump sum fixed price contract, it is not the job of the contractor, being the tenderer, to point out errors to the client, but to give the whole work price. Any error can be claimed by means of a variation so the contractor will not suffer loss. The problems arise when the contractor takes into account a known error in the client's information and costs the additional work in the bid because this will raise the tender above that of his competitors and put the contractor at a tender disadvantage. Contractors not appreciating the discrepancy will arrive at a lower tender price.

Bills of quantities are not a feature of the lump sum approach. The tenderer must measure the work from the drawings and create his own bill of quantities from which the price of the full works will be calculated.

Similarly, the tenderer must assess the necessary plant and materials needed to fulfil the requirements of the work. Any omission on the part of the contractor due to tendering error cannot be claimed by him as such losses must be borne by the contractor.

When identifying an error, the contractor will seek to pursue the claim against the client by seeking a variation such that extra cost will be charged. It is up to the client to ensure that any loss sustained by the contractor arises from the contractor's own ignorance or inefficiency and not as a result of difficulties brought about by the client, in say wrongly specifying a material or incorrectly detailing a drawing.

Provisional sums are allowed in the tender bid to cover unspecified items but, in general, the client will try to limit these; firstly to reduce any leeway for the contractor to use the provisional sum in the contract illegitimately and, secondly because the nature of the overall works should be such that provisional sums are not really needed in the cost make-up. Provisional sums are often used by the contractor to hide tender indecision and it is best from the client's viewpoint to minimise this ambiguity by making the contractor cost the works fully.

As with any form of tender, bid evaluation is an important function for the client. In practice, the lowest tender is nearly always accepted, but again it is not always pertinent to select the lowest as the low bid may hide an organisation's more devious motive for wanting to buy the work or, could contain an error in the bid itself. Any anomaly must be checked by the client for obvious reasons. Care should also be taken to evaluate any bid with excessive provisional sums and answers sought from the contractor as to why the whole works are not fully priced. The accent from the client should be to see that the price is really a lump sum and fixed price before work commences, to ensure subsequent variation and additional costs are minimised.

The advantages and disadvantages of the lump sum contract

When there is a likelihood of procuring small works under a term contract or even individually on a works order basis, the client should adopt such an approach as there is little doubt that it is more economic to do so. Where the expected complexity and volume of the work is anticipated to greatly exceed the works order limit or infringe the criteria of a term contract approach, then there may be little alternative but to let the work on a lump sum basis. The lump sum contract is a useful alternative to major tendering based on quantities as it provides a middle ground between small jobbing works and the large construction projects.

Lump sum contracts do have distinct disadvantages which are well recognised and accepted. These include:

- It is more costly to procure a lump sum contract than a works order or term contract so the client must identify if the work truly falls into the lump sum contract category.
- The approach is more complicated, requiring complete documentation, detailed drawings and careful specifications.
- The contract is fundamentally based upon the provision of full and total project information. Any discrepancy will cause variation and additional cost.
- The contractor can take advantage of discrepancies in the detail provided by the client and unscrupulous contractors may make an occupation of this.
- Provisional sums are frequently included in the tender to hide the indecision and uncertainty of the tenderer.
- Selection of the bid is nearly always based upon the lowest tender and this may not always be the most economic solution in the long-term.

References

1   Milne, R.D., *Building Estate Maintenance Administration*, (1985), Spon.

5 Forms of Contract

5.1 Contract

General

Any contract for building work is fundamentally an agreement between two parties, the client (*normally referred to in a form of contract as the employer*) and the building contractor. The basis of the contract is an offer made by the contractor to undertake the work for a certain sum of money and acceptance of that offer by the client. Building contracts are considered within a separate field of contract law to other forms of contract as the basis for the agreement is ostensibly for the supply of labour and materials and not a contract providing, for example, the sale of goods or contracts for the provision of services.

In Chapter 4, it was seen that the client might procure small building works on a jobbing basis, arranged verbally over a telephone and without reference to any form of written agreement. Conversely, the client may procure larger works on a lump sum fixed price basis using a standard form of arrangement. There is, in fact, no legal requirement for a building contract to take any particular form and agreements for building work are often made verbally. Without a confirmation of the intentions of both parties being given in writing, ambiguity in the understanding of these intentions commonly gives rise to disputes as to what has actually been agreed between the two parties.

The only sure way to alleviate some of the many problems that occur is to procure building work with reference to one of the many standard forms of building contract. Although even a definitive contract will not eliminate all the difficulties that may develop in the course of construction, even a simplistic contract will help to amplify the understanding of the terms of agreement between the two main parties, the client and the contractor.

Advantages of defined contracts

There are obvious concerns, even dangers, for the client if building works are procured without stating the basis of agreement between the client and the contractor before work commences. Without a frame of reference within which both parties can operate it is easy for ambiguity and disagreement to set in. Verbal agreements clearly give most cause for concern. Agreement in the form of letters between the parties may alleviate some difficulties, but frequently they fail to resolve deeper and more complicated disputes. Clients may present their own form of contract but this is likely to meet with the suspicion of the contractor since the form may, from the contractor's perspective, favour the client. The advantage of a standard form of building contract is that the terms and conditions of the agreement between the two parties are defined and clear, and moreover, the contract neither favours the client nor contractor since it will have been drafted by an independent body or institution and not written by one of the parties with a vested interest in the contract.

Any form of contract or agreement used in building work will be directed towards a number of basic objectives, these being to:

- Present the necessary framework and structure for the administration of the contract.
- Provide for efficient and effective management of the works to be carried out.
- Be sufficiently rigid to provide contract structure to meet the defined objectives, yet retain adequate flexibility to meet changes to those objectives.
- Achieve the contract objectives with due consideration to time, cost and quality of the works.
- Provide contingency actions to accommodate change and difficulties in the undertaking of the contract.
- Apportion risk and responsibility for the various aspects of the project to the individual parties.
- Provide coverage of risk which is not the responsibility of any particular contractual party.
- Manage disputes which arise in the course of the contract.

In general, building contracts:

'Can and should provide a practical framework to maximise the probability of success, by allocating clear provinces of responsibility to those persons within the aegis of the contract; by providing adequate powers, with effective means of enforcement, to enable discharge of powers imposed; and by providing for the timely transfer or delivery of information or decisions necessary for the fulfilment of responsibilities'[1]

Any form of contract is essentially an agreement between the client, or employer, and the contractor. Where, for example, the client appoints a consultant representative, (architect or engineer), the responsibility is only delegated to that consultant. The agreement rests between the client and the contractor.

A defined form of building contract between a client and a contractor seeks to:

- Define the obligations, duties and responsibilities of the parties.
- Establish the working relationship between the parties.
- Provide written documentation that is defined, workable and understandable by the users.
- Deal fairly with the interests of all parties.
- Reflect the reasonable expectations of the parties.
- Identify the apportionment of risk to the parties.

The range of contract forms

There are many different forms of contractual arrangement available to the client when procuring building work. Almost all arrangements have standard forms which, whilst perhaps being far from ideal, are understood within the construction industry generally, have proliferated over the years and are now well accepted. Such standard forms of building contract are available to clients in both the public and private sectors with central government and local authorities having their own version of the standard forms following those used in the private sector. There are also standard forms of contract applicable to particular geographic areas, for example contracts used in Scotland, to accommodate regional approach, customs and legal systems.

The choice of contract form in any given situation is dependent upon the consideration of a great many factors such as the type and nature of the work; the level of client knowledge and expertise; the client's requirements; time; cost; performance and quality; employment of sub-contractors and suppliers; and many other factors, some of which appear to be quite extraneous to the characteristics of the building process itself. Those factors determining choice are described and discussed subsequently. Any and all of the factors must be considered carefully and prioritised before any decision can be taken to select an appropriate form of contract.

Many forms of contract, particularly for larger construction projects, are of long standing contractual approach, reflecting the pattern of tradition within the building and construction industry. Over decades it has been customary for building clients to procure building traditionally through the appointment of a design consultant, the architect, and only within the last ten to fifteen years has there been any discernible trend towards the use of non-traditional procurement systems. Whilst traditional procurement has been dominant and remains so to a high degree, with over sixty-five to seventy per cent of building work still being procured traditionally, alternative forms of procurement and contract have emerged with the changes taking place within the industry. Perhaps the most significant aspect of change in recent times has been in the perception and understanding of the building process by the industry's clients. Clients today have a greater awareness of the building process and are more actively seeking to become involved in the process themselves. They are no longer prepared to sit back and be guided by the design consultant but want to influence the building process more themselves. Pressure from such sources has influenced the development of new standard forms of building contract, yet change is notoriously slow to take place within the building industry. The process of producing new standard forms of building contract is often tortuous, driven by commercial or economic necessity and as a result they frequently fall by the wayside for lack of support or excessive procrastination in development.

Non-traditional forms of contract have, of course, followed the different procurement systems where the relationships between the parties is fundamentally changed. Where there is a change in the working relationship of the parties, new forms of contract have been needed to define the different roles, duties, responsibilities and obligations that the parties assume.

Over the years, many forms of contract have been developed to accompany the various methods of procurement for building work. Many have, in fact, been off-shoots from existing documentation and these have been created to meet particular project requirements, such as particular cost limits or to meet time schedules and the like. A wide range exists across both the public and private sectors of the construction industry, accommodating particular sector needs in; general building; small and minor building works; renovation work; landscaping; specialist engineering; chemical; and petro-chemical industries. In the context of this review, an appreciation is needed of some of those contract forms which are relevant to small works and those procurement systems identified in Chapter 4.

5.2   Forms of contract for small building works

General

The fundamental differences between the various types of contractual arrangement relate mainly to the methods of procuring the work, the way in which it is measured and valued and the respective levels of financial risk borne by the client (*employer*) and the contractor. For small works, there are a number of standard forms of building contract in addition to the client developed forms of contracts. Even the most minor of small works, procured on what might be termed a jobbing basis, is likely to be the subject of a certain degree of contractual arrangement and documentation and even arrangements between parties made over a telephone have been known to be upheld in law.

In the context of small building works, some of the most commonly used contractual arrangements are the following standard forms of building contracts;

- Client's (*Employer's*), Terms and Conditions of Contract.
    - these are written by the employer and applicable to small building works individually procured, or measured and daywork term contracts.
- Joint Contracts Tribunal, (JCT), Standard Form of Contract for Work of a Jobbing Character.
    - simple conditions of contract for use with JCT form of tender or for use with client's own works ordering system.
- Department of the Environment, (DoE), General Conditions of Contract, for:
    (a) Measured Term Contracts.
    (b) Daywork Term Contracts.
    - applicable to small works procured under a term contract on either a measurable or daywork payment basis.
- Joint Contracts Tribunal (JCT), Form of Measured Term Contract.
    - applicable to small works procured under a term contract on a measurable basis.
- Joint Contracts Tribunal (JCT), Agreement for Minor Building Works.
    - applicable to small building projects, mainly in the private sector.
- Scottish Building Contract Committee (SBCC), Form for Minor Building Works.
    - applicable to small building projects (Scotland, predominantly), for use in both the public and private sectors.
- Faculty of Architects and Surveyors (FAS):
    (a) Small Works Contract
        - applicable to works described by drawings, specification, but not using bills of quantities for use in both public and private sectors.
    (b) Minor Works Contract
        - applicable to works carried out on a lump sum basis, for use in both the public and private sectors.
- General Conditions of Government Contract (GC), for Building and Civil Engineering Minor Works.
    - applicable to small building projects, in the public sector.

The applications of the various forms of contract to small works fall into two main categories. The first group of four are those forms of contract that are relevant to jobbing works and ordered small building works, whilst the second group incorporating the remaining four contract forms are applicable to what may be said to be small/minor building projects, although their titles tend to refer to small/minor works. The inclusion of the second group affords recognition of their individual status, shows their applications and allows differentiation between what they describe as 'small' or 'minor'.

It is not the purpose of this review to provide extended detail on all the various standard forms of contract that are available to procure and contract small works. In many cases the forms are very detailed and founded in legal complexity. Their analysis and review, therefore, is best left to the contractual and legal experts. Rather, this is intended to present a level of introduction to and familiarisation with the various forms of contract. For further information, the reader is directed to the references presented in the appendices, together with the bibliography from which other material presenting more detailed descriptions is available. This chapter does, however, review the application of the various forms of contract and progresses to discuss the factors to be considered when choosing an appropriate form of building contract for small works.

Client's (employer's) terms and conditions for contract

Small works are often procured by the client on a jobbing basis and are frequently made verbally, even over the telephone. While there is nothing to prevent a client from following this course of action, arrangements made in this way can have obvious pitfalls. Upon occasions, it is equally true to say that the jobbing approach is the most easily arranged and cost effective method of procurement from the client's point of view. A large proportion of clients will procure the services of a building contractor in this way. For members of the general public, jobbing building is by far the most used method to procure the services they require from the building industry. Most homeowners, small industrial organisations and other minor estate owners are likely to have small works, alterations, maintenance and repair from time to time and procure the necessary work by simply telephoning around to identify an available craft operative or contractor. Only rarely would such a customer be sufficiently discerning that they embark upon the inconvenience of obtaining competitive tenders for very small works. It is well appreciated that many such jobs are carried out without reference to a detailed and complete quotation and any form of contract and are paid for by cash transactions. It is equally well recognised that it is this absence of a formal arrangement between the client/customer and jobbing trades that gives rise to difficulty and dissatisfaction, which in turn, had made jobbing building, perhaps unjustifiably the scourge of the building industry. The vast majority of small works managed in an *ad hoc* way are, fortunately, accomplished without difficulty and to the satisfaction of the customer.

Even larger client organisations procure small works in an *ad hoc* jobbing fashion and whilst a one-off engagement may be considered viable and cost effective, where many small works are to be undertaken, it was seen in Chapter 4 that there are acceptable formalised procurement methods available.

Where a client procures small works on either a works order basis or daywork basis, it is likely that in addition to the basic information provided on the works/daywork order, the documentation will be supplemented by Client's (*Employer's*) Terms and Conditions of Contract. Such terms and conditions tend to be categorised by the client as applicable to the following:

- Small building works (jobbing work) contracts.
- Minor building lump sum contracts.
- Measured term contracts.
- Daywork term contracts.

Small building works (or jobbing works) contracts use specific terms and conditions outlined on the works order/daywork order itself. Minor lump sum contracts usually have accompanying model specifications and procedures whilst measured term contracts and daywork term contracts have client-developed model tender documentation and procedures. Such terms and conditions are developed by the client to meet the exact needs of the client, although they are usually based on a generic model such as the Department of the Environment (DoE)/Property Services Agency (PSA) conditions of contract or schedule of rates in the case of term contracts.

Most client's (employer's) general terms and conditions of contract address the following main contractual aspects:

- Purpose and application of the form of contract.
- Organisational proforma documentation to discharge various aspects of the contract such as instructions and variations.
- Selection of the contractor, including list of approved contractors and specifications for competitive/non-competitive tendering.
- Operating procedures for obtaining quotations, processing the individual orders and issuing instructions and variations to the works.
- Financial limits, specifying the upper limit of orders for individual works.
- Methods of certifying payment, including measurement (where appropriate) and authorising payment of interim valuations and final accounts.

It is usual to define and describe the general, and any specific, terms and conditions of contract on the reverse side of the actual works order or daywork order form. Without proceeding to detail at this juncture, it is usual to describe the terms and conditions of contract under the following headings;

- Definitions of terms used in the text of the contract.
- Contractor's obligations.
- Basis of instructions and variations.
- Method of pricing (fixed price or variable, including daywork).
- Form and method of payment.

- Working hours.
- Quality of materials.
- Level of workmanship required.
- Defects liability.
- Sub-contract arrangements.
- Safety, health and welfare.
- Protection of the works.
- Protection of existing property.
- Protection to persons on or near the site of the works.
- Damage to property on or near the site of the works.
- Insurance and financial guarantees.
- Determination of the contract.
- Confidentiality of client/contractor relationship during the contract.

As works orders and daywork order approaches are a direct form of contract between the client (*Employer*) and the contractor, there is no provision for the employment of consultants such as an architect or quantity surveyor. The terms and conditions of contract do, however, allow for the appointment of a works superintendent, works officer or works supervisor who manages the contract directly for the client. The practical day-to-day discharge of the contract including the issue of instructions and variations, agreeing work completed, assessing quality and the like is, therefore, managed by the works superintendent or supervising officer who works in association with the contractor's site manager or site foreman.

Criteria for use
Client's (*Employer's*) Terms and Conditions of Contract are developed by the client, with or without reference to a standard form of building contract and are applicable in the following instances:

(i) Where the contract is directly between the client (*employer*) and the contractor and there is no appointment of an architect or other consultant.

(ii) When procurement is based on a works order or daywork order and details are provided by drawings and/or specifications, but the volume of the works and quantities are not determined.

(iii) Where the cost of the works is estimated and does not exceed a predetermined limit or works order/daywork order value (this limit could be £500, £1000, or £2500 depending upon the nature of the small works generally undertaken).

(iv) Where the duration of the works and materials to be used are of an anticipated value but not precisely known.

In addition to the aforementioned, the Client's (*Employer's*) Terms and Conditions of Contract are developed for use in term contracts in the following situations:

(v)   Where many individual small works are to be carried out by the single contractor under one all embracing contract.

(vi)   Where a contract duration (term) is fixed, usually for three years but can be over any set term of contract such as the annual term contract.

(vii) Where the precise volume of the intended works is not known but the client can determine the estimated contract value (ECV), or estimated annual value (EAV) for the works.

(viii) Where the works are valued on a client's schedule of rates for measured works or on a cost plus daywork basis.

Joint Contracts Tribunal (JCT) standard form of contract for building work of a jobbing character

This form of small works contract, published in 1990, is a simple document for use with a JCT tender form or a client's own works order. Many employers who currently use their own works order procedure may utilise the JCT form and have only to provide the following basic information:

- Start and finish dates for the work.
- Employer's representative (to be named).
- Defects liability period.
- Minimum amount of liability insurance.

Where the JCT form is used, this is sent to the contractor with the usual project details, drawings, specifications and other control documentation. When signed by both parties, the form represents the agreement or contract. If the JCT form is not used, the client's own order becomes the necessary formal documentation.

Criteria for use
The criteria for use are the same as those specified for Client's (*Employer's*) Terms and Conditions of Contract with the following additions:

(i) May be used with a standardised contract (JCT form) or with client's own conditions, specified on the official order.

(ii) Method allows for verbal ordering of work by telephone without the price or contract period being set, although this approach should always be backed up by a written order. This flexibility, of course, assumes that the standard contract is used or that both parties are familiar with the employer's conditions.

The Department of the Environment (DoE) General Conditions of Contract

There are essentially two forms of DoE General Conditions of Contract, those applicable to:

(i) Measured Term Contracts.
(ii) Daywork Term Contracts.

The DoE General Conditions of Contract are used where the contractor agrees to carry out the works specified by the client, (*employer*) within a specified price range and for an agreed number of years, (*term*). Measured term contracts are based upon standard schedules of rates and daywork term contracts are agreed on a cost plus basis.

These forms of contract differ from the Client's (*Employer's*) Terms and Conditions of Contract in that they do not use a schedule of rates written by the client, rather they are based on a standard schedule drafted by the DoE. It is not uncommon for some clients to utilise the DoE General Conditions of Contract and substitute their own schedule of rates, this being done predominately where the work is of a specialised nature and falls outside the content of the standard schedule of rates. Both forms of DoE Contract are applicable to small works in both the private and public sectors although they are mainly used in the latter.

Criteria for use
The DoE form for measured term contracts is applicable where:

(i) Small works are to be carried out by one single contractor under an all-embracing contract.
(ii) A contract duration (*term*) is fixed, usually three years but can be any set term agreed between the client and contractor.
(iii) The precise volume and value of the work is not known but the client can determine the estimated contract value (ECV) or estimated annual value (EAV) for the works.
(iv) The works can be measured and valued on a standard schedule of rates.

The DoE form for daywork term contracts is used in the aforementioned situations but omitting item (iv) and substituting the following item:

(v) Where the works are measured and valued on daywork rates (cost plus basis using labour manhours expended, value of plant and materials plus an element of the contractor's overheads and profit).

In both the DoE measured term and daywork term contracts the individual works are authorised using the works order (foreman's order or FO) or daywork order system, as previously described. A financial limit is placed on such orders for budgeting purposes and the individual works are expected to be completed within a short duration. It is common within these contracts to set different work order/daywork order cost ranges to cover work of differing volume. For example cost ranges for orders up to: £1500; £2500; and £5000. This will, obviously, allow more extensive small works to be procured under the contract form, rather than attempting to procure an item of work over several orders or resorting to letting one item of work out to lump sum tender. The general approach to procuring small works under measured term contracts and daywork term contracts is reviewed in Chapter 4 and applies to small works contracts arranged using the DoE General Conditions of Contract.

Joint Contracts Tribunal (JCT) form of measured term contract

The application and function of this form is similar to that described under the preceding DoE Form with a number of notable and important exceptions.

  (i) It is designed for use on measurable works, although there is provision for work to be conducted on a daywork basis.
 (ii) There is a specific facility for prioritising orders according to their importance which requests different response times from the contractor.
(iii) The Form is designed to be used in conjunction with the National Schedule of Rates [developed by the Society of Chief Quantity Surveyors in Local Government – (SCQLG) and the Building Employer's Confederation – (BEC)]. It cannot be used with a PSA schedule or client's bespoke schedule.

Clauses otherwise follow the general pattern of the JCT group of building contracts.

Joint Contract Tribunal (JCT) agreement for minor building works

The Joint Contract Tribunal (JCT) Agreement for Minor Building Works is one of a group of JCT contract forms. The group of contracts are directly for use in a main contract between the client (*employer*) and the building contractor, although variations to detail allow for the contracts to be used in a variety of situations. The Form of Agreement for Minor Building Works is one of the current variations, (or 'editions' as JCT designate them), of the JCT group commonly referred to as JCT 80 from which this specific minor works contract derives its acronym JCT 80, MW or MW 80 in its usual abbreviated form. (*The figure 80 refers to the year of publication of the 'edition'*). In general, MW 80 is applicable to small building projects of greater complexity and considerably higher value than jobbing building works and is used, mainly, to procure projects in the private sector.

Criteria for use

Like all the JCT group of contracts, MW 80 is used for specific applications and therefore, five criteria determine the validity of its use, these are specified in MW 80 using the following descriptions:

(i) Where minor building works are to be carried out for an agreed lump sum and the employer (client) has appointed an architect.

(ii) The contractor's lump sum offer is based on drawings and/or specification and/or schedule without detailed measurement, (i.e. works for which no bills of quantities have been prepared).

(iii) The period required for the execution of the work must be such that full labour and material fluctuation provisions are not required, (i.e. where there is no likelihood of measured cost nor where works are complex).

(iv) Subject to the above, the form is generally suitable for contracts up to the value of £70 000 (at 1989 prices).

(v) There is no provision in the form for those situations where the employer wishes to control the selection of specialist sub-contractors.

From the criteria specified in MW 80 it is clearly evident that the form of contract is mainly for application to works that are more substantial than small jobbing works. It is unlikely that this form would be used on small works unless the work was of a substantial value and complex in nature. Essentially the approach is used on projects that are certainly larger but do not meet the criteria needed for major projects where JCT 80 would be applicable. Having said this, it is worth noting that JCT 80 MW is frequently used outside the parameters specified by the contract. For example, contracts with values over £3 million have been procured on MW 80 even though its recommended upper limit is currently £70 000.

MW 80 is suitable for application to private sector minor building work and is also used by local authorities for public sector projects. Where the building work is of a more substantial nature but where there is no bill of quantities the employer should adopt the appropriate edition of the main JCT Standard Form. Similarly, where the work is of a specialised nature or the relationship between the contractual parties differs from that traditionally experienced, again the appropriate edition of the JCT Standard Form should be consulted. As MW 80 is based in law on the legal system of England and Wales, this form should not be used for application in Scotland. Scots law is quite different in nature and, therefore, is taken into account through the issue of a separate series of contract documents by the Scottish Building Contract Committee (SBCC) which follows quite closely the framework of JCT since the SBCC is, in fact, a constituent body of the Joint Contracts Tribunal.

MW 80, like many forms of contract, follows a common format setting out the articles of agreement between the two main contract parties. The various specific clauses are grouped under the main contractual headings, as follows:

1.0   Intentions of the parties.
2.0   Commencement and completion.
3.0   Control of the works.
4.0   Payment arrangement.
5.0   Statutory obligations.
6.0   Injury, damage and insurance.
7.0   Determination (resolution of the contract when disputed).
8.0   Supplementary provision (such as provision for taxes).

There is, in addition to the Minor Works Form, an Intermediate Form of Building Contract applicable for use on contracts that lie between the Minor Works Form and the JCT Standard Form. The Intermediate Form is a lump sum form which broadly follows the layout and application of the Agreement for Minor Works. This form has in the past sometimes proved problematic and has been revised repeatedly to alleviate its main deficiencies.

The Scottish Building Contracts Committee (SBCC), form for minor building works

The Scottish Building Contracts Committee (SBCC), Form for Minor Building Works is modelled on JCT 80 MW, but explicitly takes into account the law of Scotland (*usually referred to more simply as Scots Law*) and Scottish building practices. The application of the SBCC Form for Minor Building Works is directed toward smaller building works normally procured in the private sector, although it may also be used in public sector projects. Whilst the form has developed for use in Scotland, there is no genuine reason why the contract could not be adapted to English law for use in, say England, as the basis of the contract is recognised in England. Scots Law does have its own distinctive character which is taken into account by the SBCC Form and, therefore, a specific series of documents are used in the Scottish application which makes them different from their JCT 80 counterparts. In all other respects the form of contract follows the JCT 80 MW form of contract.

The SBCC form brings attention to particular legal aspects surrounding the differences in common law between Scotland and England, for example, it considers the contract relative to the purchase of materials and goods between client (*employer*) and the contractor, and the approach towards the purchase of materials and goods between client (*employer*), contractor and subcontractor, where the law in England and Scotland considers these aspects differently.

Criteria for use

The criteria for use follow those specified for JCT 80 MW. The SBCC form has a Scottish Supplement which is highly relevant and serves three purposes:

(i) To interpret expressions in the SBCC and JCT contracts relevant to their application.
(ii) To establish which of the JCT conditions apply to the SBCC form to avoid duplication of clauses and conditions.
(iii) To review JCT conditions to the SBCC framework to take into account the unique nature and characteristics of Scots Law.

The Faculty of Architects and Surveyors (FAS) form of contract

The Faculty of Architects and Surveyors (FAS) has two forms of contract applicable to small building works. These are frequently confused, with each being used for quite different applications. These two forms are:

(i) The FAS Small Works Contract.
(ii) The FAS Minor Works Contract.

Small Works Contract

The Small Works Contract is described by the Faculty of Architects and Surveyors as being:

'intended for use with small works (such as private houses, or alterations, or extensions) described by drawings and/or specifications or a schedule of work, but not using a bill of quantities'[2]

Criteria for use

The FAS Small Works Contract is clearly not for use on complex or higher value building work since alternative and more appropriate forms of contract would be applicable. It may be used for small building work in both the public and private sectors although it is used mainly in the private sector for small domestic type construction projects. The FAS Small Works form is well favoured by the smaller consultancy practices and is therefore a well used and well accepted approach. The approach and format of the contract follows somewhat the JCT Form and, therefore, the operational characteristics and managerial procedures are similar in application.

Minor Works Contract

The Faculty of Architects and Surveyors Agreement and Conditions of Contract for Minor Works is described as:

'intended for minor works to be carried out on a lump sum basis with no nominated sub-contractors'[2]

The framework and structure of the FAS Minor Works Contract follows the pattern of the JCT 80 MW contract although particular definitions and designation of the parties differs along with the grouping of the various clauses that make up the contract. The specific description of 'advisor' rather than architect for example, allows the appointment of a surveyor in the supervisory role, an unusual approach but one the client may choose to follow if cost was uppermost in mind rather than the technological content of the work.

Criteria for use

Like the FAS Small Works Contract, the Minor Works Contract is not really intended for large and complex projects or those of a high value. These would be better accommodated by other major forms of contract within the JCT group of contract forms. The contract may be used on minor building projects in both the public and private sectors.

Neither the FAS Small Works Contract nor FAS Minor Works Contract should be confused with the FAS Building Contract form which is designed for application to larger and more complex construction projects.

The General Conditions of Government Contract, (GC) for Building and Civil Engineering Minor Works

The General Conditions of Government Contract for Building and Civil Engineering Minor Works, or GC/Works contracts, fall into two distinct categories:

(i) GC/Works/1.
(ii) GC/Works/2.

These are quite different contracts and frequently the subject of confusion. GC/Works/1 is generally used for 'major' building work with a high value (exceeding £70 000 at 1989 prices) and where a lump sum price is to be used based on bills of quantities. GC/Works/2 is applicable to smaller building projects in both building and civil engineering works where, again, a fixed price is used to determine the project cost.

Criteria for use

The GC/Works/2 contract has its origins in the Property Services Agency (PSA) and is, therefore, designed for use on PSA projects in the public sector. It is not applicable to private sector activity and is not used in the public sector generally since clients tend to use the JCT 80 MW arrangement.

GC/Works/2, in terms of format, characteristics and operation follows the

JCT 80 MW contract, but, as the form is ostensibly used by one client, – the PSA, the detailed content takes account of their own particular requirements. As a consequence, there are specific clauses and provisions that differ markedly from other shorter forms of building contracts. In all other respects, GC/Works/2 follows the JCT 80 MW form of contract. The application of GC/Works/2, along with the other forms of contract available for small/minor works is illustrated in Figure 5.1.

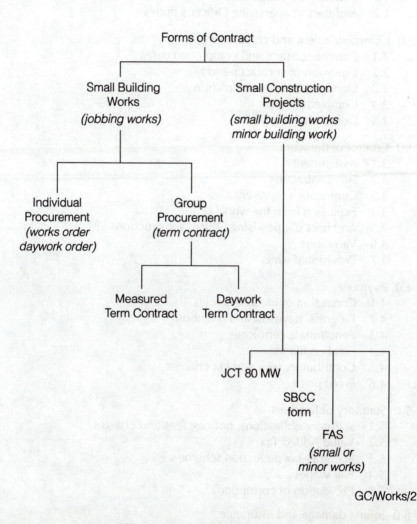

Figure 5.1 Forms of contract for small building (jobbing) works, term contracts and small/minor construction projects.

Main components of forms of contract

The shorter forms of building contract described in this chapter, with the exception of the Client's (*Employer's*) Terms and Conditions, tend to follow a set pattern in determining the detail of their clauses. Most of the forms follow the style and format of the JCT 80 MW^3 form of contract which considers the content and detail of the contract under the following sections:

1.0 Intention of the Parties
    1.1   Contractor's obligations
    1.2   Architect's/Supervising Officer's duties

2.0 Commencement and completion
    2.1   Commencement and completion dates
    2.2   Extension of contract period
    2.3   Damages for non-completion
    2.4   Completion date
    2.5   Defects liability

3.0 Control of the work
    3.1   Assignment
    3.2   Sub-contracting
    3.3   Contractor's representative
    3.4   Exclusion from the work
    3.5   Architect's/Supervising Officer's instructions
    3.6   Variations
    3.7   Provisional sums

4.0 Payment
    4.1   Correction of inconsistencies
    4.2   Progress, payment and retention
    4.3   Penultimate certificate
    4.4   Final certificate
    4.5   Contributory levy and tax charges
    4.6   Fixed price

5.0 Statutory obligations
    5.1   Statutory obligations, notices, fees and charges
    5.2   Value Added Tax
    5.3   Statutory tax deduction scheme
    5.4   Fair wages
    5.5   Prevention of corruption

6.0 Injury, damage and insurance
    6.1   Injury to or death of persons
    6.2   Injury or damage to property

6.3 Insurance of the works
    (a) new works
    (b) existing structures
6.4 Evidence of insurance

7.0 Determination
    7.1 Determination by employer
    7.2 Determination by contractor

8.0 Supplementary Memorandum
    8.1 Statutory Tax Deduction Scheme

The more important details of contract are considered in section 5.4 of this chapter, where they are described relevant to the various forms of contract applicable to small works.

5.3 Selection of contract form

General

When a client is considering the most appropriate form of contract to adopt when procuring small works, the primary and most influential factor is the type of work itself. The type of work, (its technological content and complexity) determines other significantly influential variables such as: scale of the work; the nature of construction operations; materials to be used; time to be allowed; all of which will ultimately lead one to consider the cost of the works.

In simple terms, the type of work, in many cases, intrinsically suggests an appropriate method of procurement and contractual form for the client to adopt. If an industrial customer, for example, seeks to procure the construction of a simple concrete machine plinth to locate a small floor mounted cutting machine, the client is likely to lean toward a jobbing work approach, issuing a work order supplemented by the client's terms and conditions. In contrast, a homeowner procuring a house extension through a small architectural practice would be likely to use the Faculty of Architects and Surveyors Small Works Contract. A petrochemical client requiring continuous small works alterations and repairs to parts of a large plant complex is likely to adopt a term contract approach on a measured works or daywork basis depending upon the nature of the works. The type of work, therefore, influences greatly the approach adopted.

The type of work, however, is not the sole criterion upon which the selection of contract form will be based. There are a number of important aspects which are influential. These can be considered under the following headings:

- Purpose of the contract (obligations).
- Scope of the work (type, nature and extent).
- Cost (price of the work including measurement and valuation procedures).
- Time (schedule and over-run).
- Quality (performance).
- Degree of risk (apportionment among the parties)
- Resolution of disputes (and difficulties during the contract).
- Detail of the contract (different applications and approaches).

Purpose

The purpose of any contractual arrangement is to provide the client (*employer*) and the contractor (*and any other parties to the contract*), with a legal framework within which the works can be expeditiously and correctly carried out to the satisfaction of the client and with adequate recompense to the contractor. In addition, the form of contract structures the approach and organisation for the project by formalising the inter-relationships between the various parties, specifying levels of authority, identifying communications, co-ordination and control mechanisms and opening up channels of feedback for the parties.

A crucial aspect of a construction contract is quite naturally its application to the resolution of conflict and dispute. It is interesting that, in general, the actual form of contract used on a project is rarely considered to be of much relevance to the running of the project until a dispute arises. Only then is the contract description and wording given very careful consideration and this tends to be undertaken by the legal profession and not by those involved in the construction process itself.

Scope of the works

The scope of the works takes into account any aspect which surrounds the type of work;

- Technical content.
- Construction complexity.
- Specification.
- Extent (*size of individual works, volume of repetitive works*).
- Location.

Any contract should specify the obligations of the parties and likewise, the responsibility assumed by the client. Project success is dependent, to a large extent, upon a positive relationship between the client and contractor and the free flow of information and mutual co-operation. The client should seek to provide the contractor with as much information as possible to allow a realistic tender to be compiled and submitted. All the aforementioned information subsumed within 'scope of work' should be provided by the client for this reason.

It is clear, however, that in some situations, complete details and full information will not be available to the client to pass on to the contractor for tender purposes. A term contract, for example, while outlining the general type, specification, complexity and location does not specify the precise extent or value of the work, but merely provides an estimated contract/annual value. Paradoxically, it is frequently the case that the smaller the work, the less is known about it or, indeed, provided for it. Some clients procuring small works on a jobbing basis will provide a detailed drawing, specification and budget value for the work whilst others will simply present a generalised requirement and loosely estimated value. This aspect, in many respects, lies in the knowledge and experience of the client and the trust placed in the reliability and expertise of the contractor by the client. A knowledgeable and experienced client, for example, procuring the machine plinth example once again, may be able to provide the contractor with a broad idea of the requirement from past experience. The experienced contractor will know intrinsically what the work entails and how much the value is likely to be.

Such a relationship only comes from time and experience and less experienced clients may have to resort to laboriously detailed contract descriptions and specifications just to progress the mechanisms of getting the work done, rather than invoking the contract to safeguard the legal interest of the client.

Where the contractor is allowed contractual freedom, as a result of general and broad terms being specified by the client, this places a considerably greater liability upon the contractor. Where the work is well and fully specified, this removes the pressure from the contractor, and leaves the client liable for any anomalies in the project documentation. The degree of responsibility for the works and the liability assumed by the parties has to be finely balanced to give a workable relationship between the two main parties.

In most situations, it is in the interests of both parties to set out, in advance and as fully as possible, the information surrounding the scope of the works. Whilst the volume of work may not be known fully by the client, there should be some assessment of work value. This may be in the form of an upper cost limit to works orders procuring jobbing works, an estimated contract annual value for term contracts, or an outline cost estimate for larger projects, since clearly any notional assessment will greatly influence the final cost estimated by the contractor.

Similarly, the location of the works, although frequently considered unimportant, should be appraised carefully since a geographically remote work site or difficult working conditions will obviously influence the contractor's assessment of the value. A small works job in a chemical complex for example, may not be geographically distanced from other similar work but may necessitate the operatives working in restrictive areas, safety zones or contaminated surroundings for which special provisions are required. This will increase the contractor's estimate of the cost of the works.

The scope of the work will alone, in some situations, determine the method of approach by the client and thereby determine the form of contract used. A small jobbing work in an extremely hazardous environment with high potential risk to the building operatives may dictate that the client adopts a daywork approach just to persuade a contractor to take on the work. In such situations it would not be uncommon for the contractor to demand daywork rates, plus a specially negotiated bonus scheme for rewarding workers and another additional allowance for hazardous working conditions. A client may find that there is a little option but to agree to these requests in which case the method of procurement and form of contract becomes somewhat superfluous as the contractor essentially calls the tune.

On larger projects, adopting a small works or minor works contract form such as JCT 80 MW or an FAS contract, the level and detail of information provided is likely to be greater since the various sections of the contract specify the requirements for drawings, descriptions, specifications and schedules. In such situations, the ambiguity of small works is removed as the more detailed and formalised approach is applied.

Cost

In the same way that the type of work intrinsically suggests a method of procurement and form of contract so too can the cost of the work. It would be unthinkable to use the JCT 80 MW for application to the low cost machine plinth example. One would utilise a one-off works order engagement. Similarly, one would not use a works order approach for the procurement of a £50 000 building project, but rather adopt a JCT or FAS form of contract, depending upon the circumstances. The value of the work is, obviously, determined by the type of work and, therefore, one is led back to the scope of the works as being perhaps the most influential factor.

The cost of the work is one of the prime concerns of the building client. The client will always be seeking to balance project time, cost and quality to secure the best possible value for money. When selecting a contract form, the client is, therefore, predominantly seeking a form that will maximise value for money. There will, in practice, always be a trade-off between the three main project aspects of time, cost and quality as the client tries to balance these variables. Time and quality can always be manipulated within the parameters of the project, but this will have the consequence of increasing the project cost more often than not.

While in an ideal situation the client would expect the shortest possible construction time, the minimum cost and the best possible levels of performance and quality, time and cost and quality should always be looked upon, as a feasible construction time, to an acceptable cost and to a respectable quality given the constraints of time and cost. Seen in this way it gives the client a realistic understanding of value for money.

The client is however not merely concerned with the overall project cost. Other issues arise in the pricing of works which are just as crucial to contract selection. These are:

- Time and method of payment.
- Measurement and approval of the work for payment.
- Valuation of variations to the works.
- Retention of payment for inadequate work.
- Valuation of price fluctuations (where appropriate on small/minor work projects).
- Final payment for the completed work.

The nature of individual small works, when procured on a jobbing basis, will make many of the above list somewhat irrelevant. Small jobbing works are likely to be of low works order value, say up to £2500 maximum at 1991 prices, and will have a project duration in days or weeks rather than months, with payment being made in its entirety upon completion of the works. Small works of this nature, therefore, will not be subject to terms and conditions specifying interim valuations, retentions, price fluctuation and the like. Instead the work will be undertaken quickly and effectively and finalised over a short time period. On larger projects subject to the terms and conditions of small/minor works building contracts the aforementioned aspects will however be a major consideration.

Time and method of payment is concerned with the periods at which interim measurement will be undertaken and interim payments will be made. The accepted period for interim payment under most contracts is at one month intervals (*following the monthly surveyor's/engineer's valuation*), although payment can be made by what are termed 'stage payments', where the contractor is paid for work once it has reached a certain stage of completion.

Payment is calculated by undertaking a valuation of the works completed each month. The contractor's quantity surveyor (*if employed*) will prepare an interim valuation, agreed with the client's quantity surveyor (*if appointed*) or supervisory officer and authorised by the client. The valuation will, in addition to measuring the completed works, value any materials delivered to or stored on site but which have not yet been used or fixed in the works and also take into account price fluctuations due to increased costs. The different contract forms will consider how such items are to be measured and valued.

The procedures for measuring and valuing variations must be reviewed. Variations can occur for a variety of reasons, the most common being changes in the specified quality or expected quantity of the work on site. In well defined contracts this does not cause too many problems but when a loosely defined contract is used it can give rise to difficulty over what has actually been agreed between the two parties.

Where the work undertaken is not completed to the satisfaction of the client's specification or instructions the need will exist to have some contractual mechanism to reject the works or order remedial action to rectify the works. This often accompanies a clause to withhold payment until the inadequate works are rectified. On small works it is unlikely that retention money would be retained since the sum would be insufficient to persuade a contractor to remedy the situation if the contractor really had no real intention of doing so. Instructions for handling defective work, however, would usually feature in the form of contract, indeed, defect liability is a customary term and condition even in simple works order arrangements.

On small works procured on a lump sum basis the client should give consideration to the calculation of the fixed price sum tendered by the contractor. It is not unreasonable for the client to request a breakdown of the price. Similarly, on term contracts, the client should establish the basis of the contractor's percentage additions to the schedule of rates as information of this sort affords improved budgetary and cost control.

Time

Where small works are arranged on a works order basis time constraints are rarely considered. The works, authorised on a measurable or daywork basis are designed to be carried out in the minimum possible time. Only where individual works orders consume excessive time to the point at which cost exceeds the individual works order cost limit would a problem be realised. In such a situation, a further works order could be raised to complete the work, although as highlighted in Chapter 4 the practice of issuing multiple orders to cover one item of work is not advisable and to be discouraged since, the works/daywork order approach is fundamentally based upon one order authorising one small project.

Time implications may be severe on more extensive small works where an overrun to the works schedule has a knock on effect. A client, for example letting retail shop units could be severely affected if incomplete building works forestalled the anticipated start of a lease. To accommodate such difficulties all the main forms of contract have extension of time clauses, usually linked to a damage payments arrangement. Where over-run is a serious issue for the client, this aspect should be carefully considered. Forms of contract have to be fair to both the client and the contractor in respect of extensions of time. The likely loss to the client must be reflected realistically in any damage clause and conversely, there must be some safeguard to the contractor who might otherwise fall foul of extraneous factors outside the contractor's control and for which the contractor should not be held responsible.

When considering the selection of any form of contract, the client should identify the following project factors relating to the aspects of time:

- Commencement date of the works.
- Completion date.
- Extensions to the contract period.
- Damages for non-completion.
- Defects liability.

Quality

With the selection of any form of building contract, the client will seek to safeguard the quality of the work performed by the contractor. The client will wish to ensure that all works are carried out to the project drawings, specifications and any other requirements that the client may impose. There are always 'implied terms' in forms of contract that place onerous responsibility upon the contractor to:

(i) Complete the works to the satisfaction of the client.
(ii) Complete the works in a workmanlike manner.
(iii) Ensure that all materials used should be fit for the purpose for which they are intended.

It is recognised and accepted within the building and construction industry that the management of quality is one of the most ambiguous areas of contract administration. It is frequently difficult for the contractual parties to agree upon what constitutes good quality. Contracts can really only prescribe good practices that will, as far as possible, seek to promote good quality. Quality can never be guaranteed in a construction project nor in the final building product. Terms and conditions of contract seek to encourage good quality through competent work practices such as prescribing; the appointment of quality assurance (QA) management; the use of a recognised QA system; reference to appropriate QA standards such as BS 5750, the UK's national standard for quality assurance. Quality management in small building works like other aspects of building relies, to a great extent, upon good intent in addition to good working practices and good procedures. Whilst, a form of building contract can invoke some influence over the procedures and practices, the subject of the contractual parties' integrity and the intrinsic desire to practice good quality is surrounded in ambiguity and conjecture.

To maximise the potential for better quality in small building works the client should consider those forms of contract that undertake to fulfil the following:

- Clearly define the desired standards of quality and performance from the outset of procurement.
- State unambiguously the standards required in all contract documentation.
- Define the detailed requirement for quality in all drawings, specifications and schedules.
- Clearly state the contractor's responsibility for performance and quality.
- Specify the action to be taken by the contractor to rectify any inadequacies that occur during the course of the work.
- Define realistic and achievable levels of quality in relation to project time and cost.
- Consider the method by which the client will control quality throughout the works, including inspection, measurement and testing.
- Consider how quality of the works will be protected and preserved within completed works and the works in progress.
- Consider implementation of a quality assurance system to formalise the management of quality throughout the works.

Degree of risk

The nature of small building works, like any form of building construction, carries some degree of risk, however small that risk may be. It is, therefore, essential that any form of contractual arrangement appreciates the element of risk shouldered by the various contractual parties. The nature of the contract itself contributes significantly to the level of risk. If the contract is essentially based upon the payment mechanism then there is a specific orientation to the assignment of the risk. Price based contracts, including lump sum fixed price contracts, require the contractor to assume a higher risk than a cost based contract as the contractor must include all costs, including an element of risk contingency in the total tender bill. In the cost based contract, the contractor is reimbursed for the actual cost incurred so the risk to the contractor is eased somewhat as greater risk will be assumed by the client.

Risk analysis is important to any client seeking to select a form of contract and is certainly vital to good project performance. Analysis should be a procurement priority to appreciate how the client is affected by the various contractual forms. Essentially this will focus upon how the nature of the project changes with the way in which the risk is allocated.

The client, in selecting a contract form, must seek to establish:

- A clear definition of all contract risk.
- Allocation of risk amongst the parties.
- Flexibility in risk apportioned by using different contract forms.
- Which contractual party can best manage risk when it arises.

- Who assumes overall management and financial responsibility for the risk if the risk cannot be controlled.

As the degree of risk is influenced substantially by the different payment mechanisms, the client must also appreciate the following:

- The anticipated final price of the tender.
- The basis upon which the price is determined (*cost or price based*).
- The client's anticipated involvement in the project.
- Suitability of the design and management solution in meeting desired time, cost and quality parameters.
- The realism of the tender evaluation and overall approach.

The level of risk also affects the contractor since the contract form will directly place some degree of risk in his quarter. In fixed price contracts, such as those used for small works, the risk element can be clearly defined and apportioned whilst on larger projects, in a competitive situation, the contractor has little influence over the form of contract adopted and therefore little control of the risk allocation.

Resolution of disputes

It was mentioned previously, that there is often little reference to the form of contract until a dispute arises. Essentially, all forms of contract should clearly set out the procedures to be adopted when a dispute occurs in the project. A larger building project will lay out the necessary approach, even referencing the procedure to be implemented by an independent arbitrator, to avoid costly litigation occurring. On small works, usually the relatively minor sum involved precludes such in-depth explanation or action and any disagreements are resolved, in the main, through discussion and goodwill by the parties. The essential issue for the client to remember is that the proper objective of a contract is not to avoid dispute, since disharmony will always arise and in many instances discussion and openness will be a positive influence upon project performance, but that the contract exists to effectively and efficiently 'manage' disagreement as it arises.

5.4 Characteristics of the forms of contract

General

The various forms of building contract used for small works can be quickly, albeit superficially, viewed by comparing the ways in which the following main project aspects are described and administered under the contract form:

- Type of contract.
- Contract documentation.
- Method of issuing instructions and variations.
- Method of payment.
- Managing extensions of time and claims.
- Completion.
- Determination.
- Dispute and conflict resolution.

Specific forms are selected to represent a range of activity from jobbing works, through ordered works, to small/minor building projects.

Type of contract

Client's (*employer's*) Terms and Conditions of Contract –
- a negotiated contract based on client's drawings and/or specifications and/or schedules, issued on a works order (jobbing based) or term contract arrangement (measured or daywork), for small works up to predetermined financial cost limit per order. Works are usually low value with cost limits set at say £1000, £2500 or £5000. Approach may be standardised by using the JCT Standard Form for Jobbing Works although the basic characteristics generally follow the client's terms and conditions specified.

DoE General Conditions of Contract –
- a negotiated contract on term basis (measured or daywork) with individual works procured by issue of works order or daywork order, and with the term contract value based on estimated contract value (ECV) or estimated annual value (EAV). An alternative is the JCT Form for Measured Works used in conjunction with the National Schedule of Rates.

JCT 80 MW –
- A fixed price contract used where the duration of the works is anticipated as short, based on drawings and/or specifications and/or schedules but no bills of quantities, and where the value is less than £70 000 (1989 prices).

SBCC Form for Minor Building Works –
- A fixed price contract used where duration of the works is anticipated as short, based on drawings and/or specifications and/or schedule where the value of the works is low and applied specifically to projects in Scotland.

FAS Contracts –
  - Small Works: a fixed price contract based on drawings and/or specifications and/or schedules but no bills of quantities.
  - Minor Works: a fixed price contract, based on drawings and/or specifications and/or schedules, where value of the works is low.

GC/Works/2 –
  - A fixed price contract used on smaller projects with specific application to PSA building or civil engineering contracts.

Contract documentation

Client's (*Employer's*) Terms and Conditions of Contract:

  - Terms and conditions written by the client.
  - Drawings.
  - Specification.
  - Schedules.

DoE General Conditions of Contract:

  - DoE general terms and conditions.
  - Specification.
  - Schedule of rates for measured work or daywork rates.

JCT 80 MW:

  - Terms and conditions, form of agreement plus one of the following;
  - Drawings, specification and schedules.
  - Drawings and specification.
  - Drawings and schedules.
  - Drawings only.
  - Specification and schedules.
  - Specification only.
  - Schedules only.

SBCC Form:

  - Drawings.
  - Specification, schedules or bills of quantities.

FAS Small Works:

  - Drawings.
  - Specification, schedules.
  - Bills of quantities.

GC/Works/2:

- Abstract of particulars, conditions and Agenda plus:
- Drawings.
- Specification.

Method of issuing instructions and variations

Client's (*Employers*) Terms and Conditions of Contract –

- All instructions and variations issued by client's Works Superintendent.
- Verbal instructions confirmed in writing.

DoE General Conditions of Contract:

- All instructions and variations issued by client's superintendent.
- Verbal instructions confirmed in writing.
- Instructions for individual works confirmed by works order or daywork order.

JCT 80 MW:

- Instructions issued by architect.
- Verbal instructions confirmed in writing.
- No provision of valuation of variations.

SBCC Form:

- Instruction from architect/supervisor.
- Verbal instructions confirmed in writing.
- Provision for variations and method of pricing.

FAS Small Works:

- Instructions from architect.
- Verbal instructions confirmed in writing.
- Provision for variations and method of pricing.

GC/Works/2:

- Instructions and variations issued by supervising officer.
- Verbal instructions confirmed in writing.
- Provision for variations and method of pricing.

Method of payment

Client's (*Employer's*) Terms and Conditions of Contract:

- Interim valuations at monthly intervals/or as specified by the client.
- May be final or subject to remeasurement.
- Payment within 14 days or as agreed.

DoE General Conditions of Contract:

- Interim valuations at monthly intervals/or as specified by the client.
- May be final or subject to remeasurement.
- Payment within 14 days or as agreed.
- Provision for increased costs.

JCT 80 MW:

- Interim valuations at monthly intervals.
- Payment within 14 days of issue of interim certificate.
- Subject to revision in subsequent certificates.
- No provision for increased costs (fixed price).

SBCC Form:

- Interim valuations at monthly intervals.
- No provision for cost fluctuations (fixed price).

FAS Form:

- Interim valuations at monthly intervals.
- Payment within 14 days or as agreed.
- No provision for cost fluctuations (fixed price).

GC/Works/2:

- Payment on contractor's request (not less than one month).
- No provision for cost fluctuations (fixed price).

Managing extensions of time and claims

Client's (*Employer's*) Terms and Conditions of Contract:

- No explicit provisions for extension of time or claims.

DoE General Conditions of Contract:

- No explicit provisions for extensions of time or claims.

JCT 80 MW:

- Extensions of time only while works are in progress.
- No provision for claims for disruption.

SBCC Form:

- Provision for extensions of time.
- Damages for non-completion.

FAS Form:

- Provision for extension of time.
- Damages for non-completion.
- Provision for claims for direct loss and/or expense.

GC/Works/2:

- Provision for extensions of time.
- Provision for damages and claims.

Completion

Client's (*Employer's*) Terms and Conditions of Contract:

- Completion when works approved by works superintendent.

DoE General Conditions of Contract:

- Completion when works approved by works superintendent.
- Completion of contract at end of term.

JCT 80 MW:

- Commencement and completion dates specified.
- No provision for partial possession.

SBCC Form:

- completion to architect's/supervising officer's approval.

FAS Form:

- Completion when approved by architect.

GC/Works/2:

- Completion when approved by supervising officer.

Determination

Client's (*Employer's*) Terms and Conditions of Contract:

- Determination by client.

DoE General Conditions of Contract:

- Determination by client or contractor.

JCT 80 MW:

- Determination by client or contractor.

SBCC Form:

- Determination by client or contractor.

FAS Form:

- Determination by client or contractor.

GC/Works/2:

- Determination by client or contractor.

Dispute and conflict resolution

Client's (*Employer's*) Terms and Conditions of Contract:

- No explicit provision specified.

DoE General Conditions of Contract:

- Provision for arbitration.

JCT 80 MW:

- Provision for arbitration.

SBCC Form:

- Provision for arbitration.

FAS Form:

- Provision for arbitration.

GC/Works/2:

- Provision for arbitration.

References

1 Uff, J. and Capper, P., *Construction Contract Policy – Improved Procedures and Practices,* (1989)
2 Clamp, H., *The Shorter Forms of Building Contract,* second edition, (1988), Blackwell Scientific Publications.
3 Joint Contracts Tribunal, *The JCT Agreement for Minor Building Works,* (JCT 80 MW), (1989).

6 Organisation and Management

6.1 The principal influences upon organisation and management

General

The organisation and management of small works, like that of any construction project, is a continuous activity that, in its broadest terms, commences with the client's clear notion of the work required and finishes with a satisfactory final account. The types of contract used for small works can take a number of forms from the works order approach to the use of a standard form, of building contract, as reviewed in Chapters 4 and 5. The general approach can appear most varied depending upon the many and diverse factors that influence small works, from the nature of the work itself to the form of contract. Understanding the organisation and management of small works requires an appreciation of the general principles and practices of good construction management, but moreover, the ability to relate these principles and practices to the particular, even unique, demands of small works.

Effective organisation and management for small works depends to a high degree, upon the successful management of three main project aspects, these being:

(i) Time
(ii) Cost
(iii) Quality

The primary constituents for organisation and management are illustrated in Figure 6.1.

The overall aim of any construction project is:

the design and construction of a building or structure to meet with the specific requirements of the client.[1]

This overall requirement, if no other, leads to the consideration of the three main aspects of organisation and management: time; cost; and quality (including the aspect of performance); all of which must be maintained if success in the undertaking of small works is to be achieved. The client is

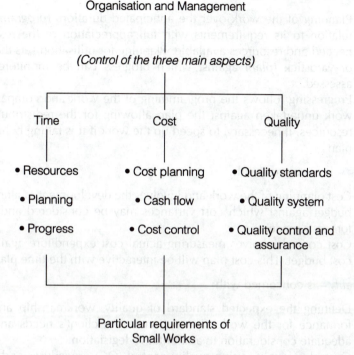

Organisation and Management

(Control of the three main aspects)

Time	Cost	Quality
• Resources	• Cost planning	• Quality standards
• Planning	• Cash flow	• Quality system
• Progress	• Cost control	• Quality control and assurance

Particular requirements of
Small Works

Figure 6.1 Organisation and management for small works

directly concerned with these particular project variables since it is these that combine to give value for money, perhaps the client's paramount objective. Small works, like any other building work must be as good as that envisaged or better. The work must also cost that which was estimated or less and the work must be completed within the time expected. It is essentially time control, cost control and quality control, around which small works management functions on a day-to-day basis and the processes of control that impart organisation to the undertaking of the works.

Control of time, cost and quality involves setting yardsticks or measures of performance in these areas against which actual performance can be compared. It also involves making decisions based upon that information and thinking about decision making for the work that remains to be done. The common feature of time, cost and quality is 'control' and all these aspects must be managed throughout the undertaking of the works to their completion if effort and activity is not to become wasteful and the works unsuccessful.

In the context of organisation and management, time, cost and quality may be described as follows:

Time – is concerned with:

(i) Planning of the work over the anticipated duration, (*programme*) in relation to its requirements with full appreciation of the resources needed and resources available. Planning for utilisation sets the basis or yardstick (*plan*) against which progress can be monitored and assessed.

(ii) Progressing follows the programming of the work and compares the work undertaken against the plan allowing for the redistribution of resources, if necessary, to speed up the work if it is falling behind the plan.

Cost – is concerned with:

(i) Cost planning of the work and involves the development of a financial budget against which cost variances may be considered and future forecasts made.

(ii) Cost control involves measuring actual cost expenditure against the cost budget. This cost plan will be interactive with the time plan.

Quality – is concerned with:

(i) Defining the expected standard of quality, workmanship and performance for the works, in relation to the client's needs and with adequate consideration to authoritative legislation.

(ii) Control of quality using quality control (QC) procedures and where necessary quality assurance (QA) systems, to ensure quality throughout the works. It also involves assessing performance of the workforce using recognised performance measures.

It must always be remembered that control of small works starts with the planning of the work, indeed, with the very notional parameters of time, cost and quality envisaged by the client. Planning, irrespective of its orientation, does not just happen because a budget or a programme or quality standard has been prepared, but rather it requires two vital inputs:

(i) That there must be a recognised plan which meets the genuine needs of the client, the needs of the work and consciously directs both the client's personnel and contractor's staff towards the main objectives.

(ii) That there must be effective arrangements used in the course of undertaking the work to ensure that people consciously work to the plan, are managed towards the plan, and can be reassigned if there is any deviation from the plan.

These aspects are of equal and vital status and importance. There would be little use in developing a programme or cost budget if they are not used for control during the work and there would be little use in specifying a quality standard if the work is not compared with and executed to that standard. It is essential, therefore, that in the organisation and management of small works that the client and contractor fully appreciate their respective performance or budgets and that their arrangements for working to these plans are well conceived and understood. Figure 6.2 illustrates the basis of small works planning and control.

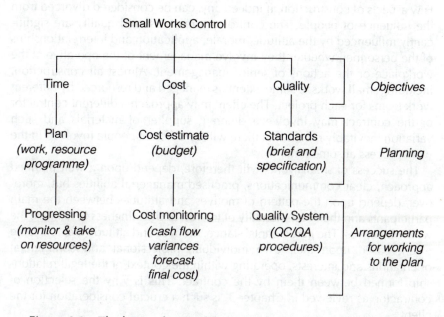

Figure 6.2 The basis of control for organisation and management of small works

It is interesting that the planning aspect nearly always forms part of the approach to construction organisation and management yet the second aspect, that of progressing, is frequently neglected and certainly understated. In simple terms, the plan must be seen as the basis of control. A plan can be wrong or incorrect in places, and often is in practice, but this is sometimes of little importance if the arrangements for working to the plan are effective. Plans can always be manipulated by effective management and good working practices.

There are also two further important principles of control in relation to time, cost and quality, these being:

(i) That there must be a warning mechanism built into any plan to highlight clearly any problems when they arise. The earlier the warning the better the effective management of variance.

(ii) That there must be sufficient flexibility in any plan to allow it to be redirected to meet changing conditions and circumstances.

If planning has these elements, then good small works management may be able to work around an inadequate plan and produce successful results.

Human aspects

Few aspects of construction, if indeed any, can be considered divorced from the influence of people. The control of time, cost and quality are significantly influenced by the attitude, morale, application and interrelationships of the personnel, whether they involve management of the operative at the workplace or the actions of senior management. Almost all construction, including small works to some extent, is managed and resourced by different work teams for each project. The client may approach a different contractor or the contract may involve a different supplier of materials and such variation inevitably means that there will be different people involved in the work process at some time.

The success of small works will therefore, depend upon a well planned approach, clear communications, practised managerial abilities but, moreover, depend upon the pattern of motives and attitudes between the main participants and their commonality of interest and willingness to achieve the work objectives. The participants' stance, motives and attitude are, to a large extent based upon their own individual, professional and commercial orientations and interests, operating within the context of the legal relationship formed between them by the contract. This is why the selection of contractor, as reviewed in Chapter 3, is such a crucial consideration for the client.

6.2   Control of time

The approach to the control of time in relation to small works can be divided into two broad aspects, organisation and management for:

(i) *Planning* – the development of a plan in the form of a small works programme to consider how the works will be undertaken in relation to time and resources.
(ii) *Progressing* – the monitoring and recording of the actual works undertaken and comparing this with those originally envisaged.

Planning

Planning is not synonymous with small works. Because of the intrinsic nature of small works they are difficult and sometimes impossible to plan for. This should not infer however that planning is inapplicable to small works. Short term planning may be useful to the organisation and management of individual jobbing works, whilst long term and medium term planning techniques are certainly recommended for small works term contracts.

The broad objective of all construction planning is to ensure, as far as possible, that work is carried out effectively and with maximum cost effectiveness and meets the genuine needs of the client and to this extent, small works should be treated no differently. It is, however, commonplace that small works are not undertaken as expeditiously as other construction work nor with maximum cost effectiveness. Two situations commonly experienced in small works management are:

- Work is inadequately carried out, necessitating the rectification of defective work, both during the work phase and after completion.
- Work is carried out beyond that level which is genuinely required to undertake the work effectively and efficiently resulting from, for example, procrastination by operatives or the over-specification of materials and construction plant.

Non-productive activity

Within the context of small works, ineffective work is likely to lead to additional time being required to carry out the work and additional cost. As discussed in an earlier chapter, work may be productive, indirectly productive, or non-productive. Ineffective work lies firmly in the latter category.

Non-productive activity within small works can result from:

- Lack of clear definition and planning of the works by the client.
- Inadequate communication of work detail from the client to the contractor.
- Poor understanding of the client's needs by the contractor.
- Poor site management by the contractor as the work proceeds.
- Lack of applicable skills by the operatives.
- Time wasted by the workforce due to ambiguous instructions.
- Lack of motivation and incentive for the workforce.
- Absence of effective management and supervisory systems to review the programme regularly, making progressing ineffective if not impossible.

For small works to be successful, these general issues and aspects particular to small works, discussed subsequently, must be appreciated, organised and managed.

The planning system

An effective planning approach for small works involves both the client and contractor. Together they must address three main aspects:

- The client clearly formulating the requirements for the work.
- The client, (*or architect if applicable*), accurately presenting these requirements in terms of drawings, specification and contract documentation.
- The contractor accurately translating the client's instructions, through the physical building process on site, into the finalised product.

The interest and approach toward planning adopted by the client and contractor will, obviously, be different although their objectives and procedures will be interactive in nature. The client will be concerned, initially, with the internal procurement procedure and management of proposed works. This will involve: the decision to use direct labour or appoint a contractor; if contracting the works, planning for tendering and contractor selection; assessing whether the contractor has the resources; and can the contractor fit the work into the available time and cost framework.

The contractor, in contrast, is interested in how the works will be resourced and can the work be done cost effectively from his standpoint. This principally involves considering the use of labour, plant and materials. It can be seen that while some aspects are different there is also some commonality between the client's and contractor's interests. The various different approaches are reviewed subsequently in application to particular types of small works organisations.

The particular requirements of small works upon planning

All of the aspects listed are those particular requirements of small works which make their planning difficult, these are:

- *Nature and scale* – Small works are, by definition, small and do not lend themselves to continuity and economies of scale. The perceived nature of small works make their organisation and management particularly difficult since it can be problematic to plan accurately for such small quantities of work. Even though small quantities are involved, the work may still necessitate the input of a variety of trades and their inter-relationships within the programme can be difficult to envisage.
- *Diversity* – Small works are greatly diverse in nature. The work may entail cutting an opening in a wall costing only a few pounds to building an entire structure costing thousands of pounds. With such a diversity of work type and differing quantities it is virtually impossible to prescribe an ideal planning mechanism to cater for all small works. While the broad principles of planning may be applied to small works, particular planning methods need to be adopted to plan and progress specific types of small works and the specific ways in which these are arranged.
- *Operational approach* – Planning for any aspect of construction requires the determining of the most efficient and effective work sequence and small works demand likewise. A plan must appreciate the inter-

dependency of trades and operational sequence, which can be especially difficult given the small value for each trade task. Moreover, there are likely to be multiple works, on say a term contract, and a number of small works will proceed simultaneously. Work programmes. therefore, must consider individual works relative to other ongoing works.

- *Discontinuity* – Where small works require an input from many different trades considerable discontinuity can result. Work is often discontinuous because the interdependency of trades requires operatives to make several or more separate visits to the workplace to complete their task. Planning for their expeditious completion, allowing for complicated trade interrelationships, is difficult where working time is to be kept to a minimum.

- *Uncertainty* – Small works are so often of an uncertain or even unknown content before they are commenced and therefore, they may be poorly described, badly documented and inadequately procured. Where small works are part of a term contract, little, if anything, is specified at the start of the contract and the work's true nature is only revealed as the contract proceeds. Accurate planning therefore, can be impossible.

- *Location and dispersal* – Planning requires an accurate perception of the work location and, where there are multiple sites, the dispersal of the workplaces. This is particularly important in considering the transportation of resources, but also in the supervision of the work since good supervision is vital to the efficient and effective undertaking of the works.

- *Disproportionate temporary requirements* – Small works, in particular if they are remote, may require a temporary workplace organisation and facilities that are grossly disproportionate to the scale of the job itself. While mobile small works gangs may alleviate this to some extent, there will always be some works that are simply too small in content to justify the resource input.

- *'Buildability'* – Whilst buildability, the extent to which the design of a building or structure aids the ease of construction, is likely to be considered seriously on larger projects, small works do not lend themselves readily to the propensities of buildability. The small scale of the work will generally make serious examination of buildability in design and construction planning cost prohibitive. When small works entail a design office input however, simple aspects of design rationalisation may be considered appropriate by the client, in particular where, in a term contract, there are many small works of a similar nature to be planned and carried out.

- *Attitude* – There is frequently an attitude amongst contractors that small works are, because of their nature and characteristics, inferior forms of work to more lucrative and prestigious construction projects. Negative attitudes can prevail in all aspects of small works procurement and management, none more so than in planning. The nature of small works usually demand that planning is kept to a minimum because it can be an involved and costly activity and a contractor who engages in accurate but time consuming planning at the tender stage may not always be successful in securing the contract.

Prioritising small works

The client will always consider the procurement of small works within a notional cost range and time framework. The time allotted for the works will differ according to the client's perception of urgency. The level of urgency is important to the contractor who must respond quickly to the client's requirements. Any procrastination in response time is likely to lead not only to increased cost for the client but also inconvenience. Most clients will, therefore, broadly group their work into categories of urgency and the contractor will, similarly, respond to these degrees of urgency. The categories are:

(i) *Immediate response (emergency work)* – is often of an unforeseen nature and work which must be dealt with immediately if severe inconvenience and cost implications are to be avoided. Some clients require an emergency call-out facility to deal with such urgent works although these would usually occur in the maintenance and repair category rather than new small works. Emergency work would usually need to be dealt with on a same day service basis.

(ii) *Urgent response work* – This is likely to be repair work which if left unattended may lead to a long term building defect. New small works could be urgent however, if they affect the progress of other works. An urgent piece of work could be regarded as work requiring attention within four to five days.

(iii) *Routine response work* – This includes small works where, once planned usually among other programmed works, they would be carried out as an ongoing part of an annual contract or term contract approach.

The prioritising of small works by the client can pose a number of problems for the busy contractor:

- Emergency and urgent works may have extremely short lead-in times making planning and resource scheduling difficult, sometimes even impossible.
- Redeployment of resources to undertake more urgent works can leave some small works undermanned whereby other works are generally disrupted by urgent works. Again planning for such activity is extremely

difficult.

- It may be difficult to resource urgent works if construction plant and materials are not in store or available at short notice. It may not be possible to even draw resources from other works if a particular item of plant, for example, was required.

Programming

In order to meet the various general and particular requirements, the different managerial approaches, forms of contract, and to accommodate the differing priorities for small works, a range of planning approaches are desirable.

Such programmes may be:

- *Long term* – these may be up to three years in duration to plan for small works undertaken under a term contract.
- *Medium term* – these are one year or annual programmes to plan small works undertaken under an annual term contract, or may be programmes planning individual small works over a long period.
- *Short term* – these may be six monthly, monthly, weekly or even daily programmes to schedule individual small works and also to accommodate, where appropriate, those works in the emergency and urgent categories.

Long term programmes

The main objective of long term programming for the client is to provide a broad overview or framework within which the works can be carried out. It is not a mechanism that specifies precise dates and durations for the work. The broad plan seeks to establish a structure and policy for the successful undertaking of the works. Long term planning, therefore, aims to:

- Establish the client's general policy and approach to undertaking small works.
- Determine the extent and schedule of the works to determine a cost outline and assess implications upon cash flow.
- Spread the work evenly over a period of expenditure (*over the year for an annual contract, over three years for term contract and over a set accounting period for individual small works*).
- Decide if in-house direct labour might be viable or whether contracting out would be more practical and effective.
- Determine the client's resources necessary to procure, design and manage the works.
- Consider the implications of the programme to the client's organisation and other activities.

For the contractor, long term programming will allow the contractor to:

- Formalise and record the planned and agreed intentions with the client, where appropriate, as for example on a term contract.
- Determine the overall timetable for scheduling and deploying resources.
- Establish the plant items and materials that will need to be procured to resource the work.
- Consider the sequence and interrelationship of works where multiple small works are to be conducted on the same or different sites.
- Prepare for progressing the works by providing a means of comparing actual work with the programme.

It may also allow the contractor to prepare better ways of managing the personnel aspect of the staff and workforce by:

- Providing a basis for cost and bonus incentive schemes.
- Assessing the performance of managerial staff for future works.
- Provide for planned training of staff and operatives.

Essentially, the client will require a broad overview or master programme approximately scheduling the work over time and, more importantly, relating activity to cost expenditure. The exact nature and extent of small works is unknown to a large degree, but nevertheless the client will wish to distribute the anticipated work over the predetermined time period and to an approximate budget. While this may be somewhat inaccurate, the client should be able to estimate within five to ten per cent of the actual value from experience and historic records of previous small works.

The way in which the programme will be presented differs from other construction projects since one is not concerned with the breakdown and sequence of operational aspects but rather concerned with the start dates and duration for the whole of an individual small works job and its interrelationship with other works. Although the long term programme itself can take many forms depending upon the type of work to be undertaken, the Gantt (*bar*) chart is usually favoured since it is the commonest, most readily understood and most accepted method for diagrammatically presenting planning typology. A typical small works bar chart is illustrated in Figure 6.3.

Such long term programmes follow the typical format of a master or overall construction programme although the item descriptions are restricted to whole small works items. The client gives an overview of what might be expected to be the main small works over a predetermined time period. Inevitably, additional small works will be required at some time. Even on a well planned long term programme for term contracts, extra or unforeseen works will occur and must be accommodated within the programme. The important aspect for the client is that the programme presents an outline of the main items which can then be related to expenditure. This can also be shown on the programme if required. As with all bar charts of this nature, the anticipated works are recorded on the programme in relation to 'real time' by estimating their duration relating to calendar dates and not merely project weeks. The programme should also appreciate any periods of non-working such as annual statutory and regional trade holidays and work duration should always incorporate an element for contingencies to allow for some measure of delay and disruption. Most importantly, there must be a degree of flexibility within the programme to allow for unforeseen and, therefore, unplanned small works to be incor-porated within the programme at short notice.

The client's long term programme, if presented to the contractor, should always be treated with respect. The programme is only an estimate of activity and should not be used meticulously as the basis for resource scheduling. It does, however, provide an outline against which resources can be tentatively planned and the labour force approximated. As the small works will only be announced to the contractor through works orders as the contract proceeds, the contractor will never know precisely when the works will be instructed and as a consequence accurate long term planning is difficult. Often, the contractor is notified of the works at short notice and may have to redeploy operatives quickly from other contracts to meet the works demands. This can have severe knock-on effects to the contractor's planned schedule of activity. It is therefore, essential that the contractor carries some additional resources to meet unexpected works.

Where a more substantial work item is required by the client, as for example the new sub-station listed in Figure 6.3, the contractor may develop a detailed programme describing the elements involved for use by the contractor's staff and operatives. This may take the form of a 'Section (*or phase*) programme' which is a closely detailed plan of work for a particular work item identifying the operations involved, their sequence and can be further developed to indicate resources and expenditure required for the work. Section programmes aim to:

- Determine the duration and pattern of the work more accurately then the long term programme.
- Determine the operational sequence in detail.
- Establish the resource requirements more precisely.
- Provide an accurate schedule for plant and material procurement.
- Make provision for detailed progressing of the work through recording mechanisms in the programme.

Medium term programmes
The principal objective in medium term programming is to provide a more accurate assessment of the small works resources and scheduling re-quirement than that presented in the long term forecast. Medium term programmes would be used, for example, on an annual term contract or to

Client/contractor small work programme

H Holiday

Month	Jan	Feb	March	April	May	Cont'd
Week ending	5 12 19 26	2 9 16 23	1 8 15 22 29	5 12 19 26	3 10 17	Cont'd
Contract week	1 2 3 4	5 6 7 8	9 10 11 12 13	14 15 16 17	18 19 20	Cont'd
Works order item		Anticipated schedule & durations				
Pipe rack bases main pipe trench	H—					
Stanchions Section C	H —					
Machine plinths Section A	H—					
Door openings Main workshop	H	—				
New sub-station Section F	H		—			
Drainage trenches Section A	H					
Acid resistant tiling Small workshop	H	—				
New car park Main compound	H			—		
Duct rails Nr 3 stores	H				—	
New fencing Compound C	H					
Drain diversion main road east	H				—	
Office refurbishment Offices 1-7	H	—	—		—	
Estimated cost						
Actual expenditure						

Figure 6.3   Client or contractor's long term programme for small works planning

plan for individual small works over a longer period if their nature was known. This programme forms the basis for considering both the physical activity and cost expenditure in relation to time. Medium term programmes seek to:

- Distribute the anticipated small works over the predetermined period of expenditure.
- Provide a continuous and uniform pattern of activity over the medium term.
- Consider the work requirements and their implications to the client organisations.
- Consider if direct labour is viable for the client or should the works be contracted out.

Although medium term programme are used mainly in annual term contracts they can be used successfully for planning individual small works where they allow provision for:

- Developing a client's framework and calendar for procurement.
- Specifying dates for the provision of design information, where applicable.
- Tendering by contractors.
- Differentiating elements of specified works from general works.

Medium term programmes are used by the contractor to plan for any of the aspects described under long term programmes but because they give greater detail medium term programmes are also used by the contractor to:

- Consider the composition of the workforce more carefully and more realistically in relation to ongoing and future works.
- Alter the composition and deployment of the workforce more readily to accommodate change in the type, nature or specification of the works.
- Consider the purchase or hiring of plant items and stocks of materials more closely to avoid unnecessary plant holding or over-stockpiling of materials.

As with long term planning programmes, the client is likely to plan only for the anticipated major works and therefore, time and cost should be allowed for unforeseen other works. Appreciating the main small works jobs should provide the client with sufficient information to consider whether to use direct labour or contract out the work. Medium term planning also allows the contractor to plan for his resource utilisation more thoroughly. Again, this may be successfully achieved, basing the plan on the main items, only allowing for a small percentage fluctuation in workload to accommodate unforeseen and additional works.

Short term programmes

Short term planning includes:

- Monthly programmes (*may be up to six months, depending upon circumstances*).
- Weekly programmes.
- Daily programmes.

For planning and programming to be effective its activity must be continuous and range from a strategic overview of the work, provided by the long term programme, to daily activity at the workplace. To achieve this continuity, there must be regular short term planning by the contractor. It is essential, not only in scheduling and resource levelling of the contractor's workforce, but also in providing feedback to the client.

Short term planning should aim to fulfil the following objectives:

- Subdivide the long term and medium term programmes into more manageable and intelligible programmes at site level.
- Provide for a more accurate assessment of the time and cost resources.
- Allocate foremen and work gangs to the works.
- Allow for closer management of the work and workforce.
- Enable management to look ahead to see forthcoming delays and disruptions and manage problems as they arise.
- Review progress of the actual work in relation to plan.
- Provide for better working methods through detailed work study, again, with reference to the plan.
- Provide feedback for both the contractor and client to assist management of the ongoing work and provide feedback for record purposes and future works.

Monthly programming for small works involves the contractor in preparing a detailed a plan of work for the month ahead. On a term contract, this may involve the review and scheduling of all those works orders and daywork orders currently open and allocating work gangs to their completion. Each order will need to be considered individually and also in relation to other outstanding orders to ensure that; all information necessary to process the work has been received from the client; that adequate labour and plant are available; that materials are in stock; and that any anticipated problems have been discussed with the client.

The work will be undertaken for the period of the plan and reviewed to ascertain its status. As one month's work is reviewed so the next month's is planned as an ongoing process. For each open works order, it may be necessary for the contractor to issue a work list to the foreman with specific instructions for the works so that the foreman may too plan the work ahead for the operatives. As additional orders are raised by the client these may be added to the contractor's programme and the foreman's list as required to keep the work within a planned framework. As orders are completed they may be ticked off the foreman's list, recorded as finished on the programme and notified to the quantity surveyor to undertake final measurement and valuation for the work on that order. Where individual small works are undertaken almost continually the contractor may use weekly or compile daily work lists to manage the work ahead. Again, the purpose is to instruct the workforce to the task and also to provide for effective and close control of the works so that both planning and progress may be an ongoing activity.

Effective planning can help to alleviate many of the problems experienced with small works:

- *Resource utilisation*
  Planning allows the client to consider how best to organise the work and allows the contractor to deploy and manage the resources more efficiently and cost effectively.
- *Setting priorities*
  Planning allows the client to establish the prioritisation for the work and allows the contractor to consider the appropriate sequence of works to meet the priorities within project constraints.
- *Purchase and stock control*
  Planning allows the contractor to define his holding of plant and materials according to the genuine needs of the works.
- *Queueing*
  Planning enables both the client and contractor to appreciate the effect of one individual small work item upon other small works in relation to scheduling and resourcing.
- *Decision making*
  Planning allows for better client and contractor decision making since planning provides more detailed information than might otherwise be available.
- *Organisational direction*
  Planning directs the workforce towards the organisational objectives of the contractor and in so doing, towards the needs of the client.

Effective small works planning has a beneficial effect not just upon the control of time and cost, although this is vital, but moreover, upon leadership and morale. The success of planning and programming depends, to a high degree, not just upon the mechanism of the planning technique but upon the attitude and acceptance of management and the workforce. A plan that is well conceived and well understood will be a positive morale booster whereas a poor plan, allowing resources to be wasted and directing the workforce inadequately, can only lead to a dispirited workforce, apathetic management and poor performance by all concerned.

Progressing

There is a general tendency in planning to believe that once the programme has been developed, all that remains to be done is to activate works in sequence to the plan until all the works are completed. In reality of course, there are a great many interrelated activities which need to take place in order to progress the work to the programme. The resources must be mustered and deployed, materials have to be purchased, information to be gathered and the works monitored and managed. It is commonplace and therefore, not difficult to illustrate work activities on a bar chart, but this will be of little use unless the plan is used to good effect in progressing the work. Moreover, the plan should give an early warning of problems and as action is taken to resolve these problems, this should form an integral part of progressing the works. It is the consistent use and update of the programme that helps to encourage their use as an all important warning mechanism during construction.

A number of standardised, well used and well accepted methods of programming and progressing are used in construction but not all are useful or successful in application to small works. Such methods are:

- *Networks*

    These are diagrammatic representations of construction, loosely based on mathematical input.

    Networks provide a framework for assessing the complex inter-relationship of activity between construction operatives or work items. In general, they are too complex and demanding for small works planning since small works are not conducive to such detailed planning analysis and only the whole works are planned in any case, not the constituent parts. Also networks are not the best method of communicating planning information to the workforce due to their level of complexity.

- *Milestone diagrams*

    These relate the achievement of activity to stages of the work or to 'milestones'. They can be useful for small works if the works are sufficiently extensive, but usually small works are completed in such a short time period that milestones cannot play a part in the progress.

- *Bar charts (Gantt charts)*

    These are most favoured for small works as their format and production is readily assimilated by the client, the contractor's management and the workforce.

The most appropriate policy towards programming and progressing small works is to use a simple mechanism and basic level of detail and expand the detail as and when required. This will ensure, as far as possible, that the methods used for planning the works will be understood. There are a number of key aspects to progressing small works, these are:

- Collect information on the progress of small works on a regular and methodic basis, update the programme as an ongoing activity and consider any changes to the plan that need to be made to effectively manage the remaining work.
- Determine the implication of either taking no action to alter the plan or taking action to reschedule the works.
- Identify if there are alternative strategies to be considered to improve the management of future work based on past experience.
- Decide what is the most appropriate future action for the works and consider the implications of this upon the resources of the organisation.

The updating cycle for planning should be related to any review mechanism that is to be adopted, such as the monthly progress meetings, if appropriate. In terms of small works, the updating cycle is crucial since the duration of small works is generally short, and therefore, reviews must be at close intervals, weekly rather than monthly. Any procrastination in the update will make the planning activity futile. Planning and progressing must be continuous and dynamic to be worthwhile and must always facilitate honest analysis and realistic decision making if it is to be truly successful.

6.3   Control of cost

General

The control of cost is the second important aspect of small works organisation and management. Cost control of small works is primarily concerned with the following:

(i)   Cost planning or budgeting.
(ii)   Cash flow forecasting.
(iii) Cost variances.
(iv) Cost assessment and recording.

As with the control of time, the control of cost must be considered from both the client's and contractor's viewpoint. Cost control will be significantly influenced by a number of general factors and again, those factors specifically related to the nature and characteristics of small works themselves.

Many small works will be undertaken on an individual basis using those methods of organisation and management described in Chapter 4. This includes the client procuring small works on a jobbing basis, using little or no formalised procedure or a works order approach with a minimum of project information. Such applications will not require the preparation of detailed cost control mechanisms such as a cost budget or cash flow forecast. The principal issue for the client will be when can the work be carried out and approximately how much will it cost. Since the duration of small works is usually limited, there is simply little need to indulge in extensive and costly financial control, rather a one-off sum of money will be reserved by the client for payment when the work is completed. If the client has a number of small works, procured on an individual one-off basis, organised under a term contract, or let competitively by lump sum tender, then the client is more likely to appreciate the significance of cost and therefore, consider a formalised method of cost control.

Types of cost control

In the same way that planning philosophy, approach and procedures will change according to requirements and circumstances, so too will cost control. The client may have need for:

- *Long term cost control* – when expenditure needs to be planned for over an extended period, as would be the case in a three year term contract, long term cost control will be essential. Although the exact amount of work is unknown and therefore, the cost is unknown, the client can still estimate the contract value (ECV) or annual value (EAV) of the works and develop a broad cost framework for expenditure over time.
- *Medium term cost control* – may be required on an annual term contract or where the client has a number of small works to procure on an individual basis. A cost plan will be useful for controlling expenditure over the term or during a set accounting period.
- *Short term cost control* – individual small works may be estimated in advance, over, say, a six month block so that the client has a pattern of likely expenditure over a given time period. This can be refined with short term cost plans to provide close cost budgeting on a monthly basis. Small works may be broken down into labour and material constituents or specialist or general works to assist analysis of particular aspects of the work. These short term estimates can form the basis for comparison of the actual costs incurred in performing the works. Information of this nature can also provide a cost record for future cost control.

The implication of small works upon cost control

- *Nature and scale* – small works are often difficult to estimate for and price accurately due to their small scale. Since the works are so piecemeal, some elements of cost can be easily over-estimated and increase the cost disproportionately to volume.

- *Diversity* – as small works are so considerably diverse in nature, it is difficult to estimate probable cost accurately from past experiences. There can be quite marked cost differences between what appears to be similar work items.
- *Uncertainty* – small works present great uncertainty since their nature and volume is generally unknown when procured. Minimum information may be provided by the client, with the contractor receiving little, if any information in the way of accurate specification, drawings and documentation. In consequence, the contractor may find it virtually impossible to price the work realistically.,
- *Term approach* – when term contracts are adopted by the client to procure multiple small works, the client is, frequently, unsure of the extent of each individual job and only the estimated contract value (ECV) is known, and then, only approximately. This can make close cost estimating and control difficult.
- *Duration* – small works usually have uncertain durations although their general completion times are short. This lack of a clear time element makes resource input difficult to estimate accurately.
- *Labour expenditure* – when considering resource inputs to small works it is difficult and often almost impossible, to differentiate between what constitutes productive work, indirectly productive time and non-productive activity as past records generally only provide a record of total manhour expenditure. Anomalies in progressing can lead to wide ranges of cost for small works which appear similar in content.
- *Feedback and recording mechanisms* – small works tend, in the main, to provide little feedback on the efficiency or effectiveness of the workforce or its management. It is therefore, extremely difficult to provide estimates for future works which ensure cost effectiveness. At times, one is simply recording the cost and no more.

Direct labour cost control

The client will seek reliable and accurate cost control in the organisation and management of small works in a number of situations, perhaps none more so important that when direct labour is to be used. A formalised cost control mechanism will allow the client to monitor, assess and review the effectiveness of the direct labour complement and continually appraise its value within the context of the client organisation. The client will wish to consider the following:

- The anticipated manhour input to individual small works to establish if it is more cost effective to employ direct labour or contract out future works. For this reason, the client organisation will treat the direct labour force as an external entity and may require estimates from the direct labour group which can be compared to outside contractors. The client organisation may reduce costs in this way by making direct labour competitive with other contractors.

- Anticipated durations and costs to form the basis for programming the proposed works and for scheduling resources and preparing associated cost budgets.
- Appreciate any changes to the programme or resources to make the work more efficient and cost effective, in particular when the direct labour is in competition with outside contractors.
- The actual manhour expenditure and cost incurred to compare against the planned expenditure to assess its real level of cost effectiveness.

Whereas the client will be able to derive an extensive database from direct labour through close monitoring, recording and feedback mechanisms, when the client employs contracted labour very little feedback will be obtained. This makes future comparison of direct labour against contracted labour a difficult task and one that is far from precise and reliable.

Cost planning or budgeting

For term contracts and the lump sum approach to the organisation and management of small works, the principal mechanism of cost control is the budget. The budget is, fundamentally, a financial statement of the organisation's policy for a given financial period and provides a yardstick against which actual costs can be compared and evaluated. It is, in essence, a method of relating expenditure to the resources available. Budgets are determined according to the contract requirements but it would be appropriate to have an annual budget in keeping with the financial year and accounting periods.

On larger term contracts of three years duration, it would still be usual to have an annual budget equating to the estimated annual value (EAV) for the contract and this would operate within the estimated contract value (ECV). The useful aspect of an annual budget is that it can be linked easily to shorter term cost control mechanisms and will be more appreciative of cash flow conditions than a three year cost budget. As cost control is usually a function of accounting practices, it is normal for cost control to be undertaken outside the organisation and management of the technological aspects of small works. It is, however, more desirable and useful if cost control comes within the remit of the supervisor directly responsible for the work. In this way, management becomes more aware of the cost implications of the decisions that it takes to progress the works (see Figure 6.4).

The real advantages of cost control will not be realised if procedures are not invoked to assess performance of the works in cost terms, although performance must always be considered in the light of time expenditure and

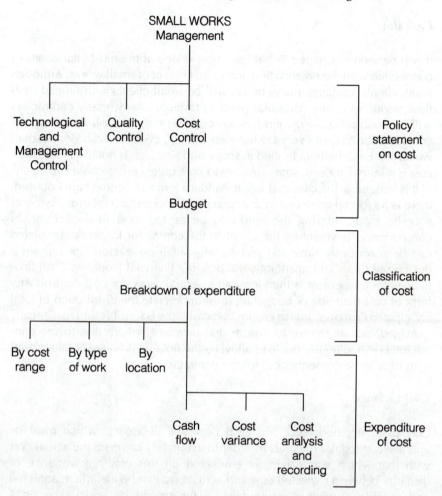

Figure 6.4   An overview of the process of cost control for small works

quality of the finished product. The breakdown of expenditure from the overall budget may comprise a review of the detailed cost of small works by cost range, work type or location but this is perhaps somewhat immaterial to the basic issues which are to establish that:

- There is a cost plan.
- Activity should be related to the cost plan.
- Performance should be measured against the plan.
- All variances to the plan be clearly identified and recorded during progressing.
- Action is specified to meet changes and variance to the plan.
- The plan is maintained and updated to meet the requirements of the future works based upon what has gone before.

Cash flow

It will be seen in Chapter 7 that cash flow is one of the most vital issues in connection with the organisation and management of small works. Although many clients are large, many others will be small clients with limited cash flow resources at any particular point in time. Similarly, many contractors will be small privately owned businesses, where again, cash flow is a vital consideration to their everyday business trading, even survival. Whilst small works are, by definition, limited in scope and size, that is not to say that their cost is minimal, indeed, some small works are quite considerable and costly.

It is frequently the case that when standard forms of contract are not used, there is no formal guideline in the agreement upon which interim payments may be made, leaving the works to be costed as a final account. In consequence, payment by the client to the contractor for work completed can be notoriously slow and place many small contractors not only in a position of financial uncertainty, but possibly financial jeopardy. Cash flow financial management is therefore, an essential aspect of cost control. Any form of cost planning or budgeting must appreciate the distribution of total anticipated cost over time to ensure that cash flow is sensibly and realistically managed, but moreover, to ensure that payment, where due to the contractor, is expeditiously made to alleviate the notable problem of late receipt with its adverse consequences for the contractor.

Cost variance

Cost planning, budgeting and cash flow are all aspects which must be appraised at regular intervals in order to accurately compare the actual cost with that which was originally envisaged. In this way any variance or disparity between expected cost and actual cost can be identified, analysed and suitable corrective action taken. This should be undertaken on a monthly basis throughout the annual or term contract or as and when required for other works.

For individual small works the actual cost presented in the contractor's final account should always be compared with the estimate, this being the contractor's tender figure, or alternatively be checked against the client's works order estimate. Any variance between the cost and estimate should always be examined to ascertain why additional expenditure has accrued. While it may be too late to prevent cost wastage on that work item the information will be useful for assessing the cost effectiveness of future works.

Where there is an annual or term contract budget, accurate cost appreciation and variance reporting will be able to establish:

- Where there is excessive cost, (*underestimating*).
- Where there is too little cost, (*over estimating*).

Either situation may necessitate changes in the organisation and management of the works. Such anomalies, particularly in the former category, may occur due to:

- Inaccurate small works estimates.
- Changes in the work conditions.
- Unforeseen increased cost of labour or materials.
- Inefficient management of the works.
- Unanticipated difficulties leading to a disproportionate amount of non-productive activity.
- Wastage of materials.
- Inappropriate use of construction plant.

Cost assessment

Cost control systems, even where carefully formulated and applied can suffer from a number of problems, these are:

- Few, if any, cost control systems can be assessed in terms of effectiveness of decisions taken by management.
- The control system itself often has an effect on the cost it seeks to control. If the mechanism is complex it is likely to be expensive and be more difficult to operate.
- There is often disparity between the management of the work and cost control. Both should be linked for cost control to be truly applicable and effective.

From the first notional idea of small works by the client, cost control requires that the work be divided into elements whose cost can be accurately predicted and represented in a cost plan. Whatever the definition applied, it is essential that the elements of work, be they labour or materials, are self-contained figures which can be checked with the actual work undertaken and any disparity between the two identified. It is also useful if cost control is not the function of an accountant or other person distanced from the work, but is rather the responsibility of the manager of the works. On term contracts for example, the client's work superintendent will be responsible for cost in addition to the design, technological and management supervision, although he is likely to be assisted by a design engineer and quantity surveyor where appropriate.

Cost assessment must provide information to the contractor's site management in order to promote quick response and action to problems and moreover, to make managers aware of the likely consequences of their actions. This can be achieved in one of two ways:

   (i) Comparing the actual cost with the anticipated cost of the works, both finished and ongoing.

  (ii) Comparing the current estimated cost with the original estimated cost.

Any assessment of cost should always be formally updated by both the client and contractor at regular intervals, usually at the monthly progress meetings, where applicable. Any variance in cost between estimated and actual should be discussed although anything learnt can only be applied to future works and not on the work completed. Actual measures of productivity should also be established, and these are considered subsequently.

Cost recording

Cost recording for small works can be as simple or as elaborate as both the client and contractor may desire. Budgets and cash flow forecasts may take the form of cost spreadsheets, cost matrices, and cost distribution curves, in fact any form of graphical representation of cost expenditure against time. Such approaches, however,do suffer unequivocally from a general lack of understanding by some levels of management and the workforce and for this reason, if no other, simpler approaches tend to be adopted. Figure 6.3 illustrates a typical bar chart for time allocation to small works and this can be easily adapted to show cost expenditure. Alternatively, simple estimated/ actual cost tables can be used to record the cost expenditure on the works. These are illustrated in Figures 6.5 and 6.6. This is a simple and clear method showing the relative difference between planned works and actual expenditure on these works and breakdowns show in which categories cost has increased or reduced.This method not only records the status of individual works but presents a profile across the range of small works, as for example being undertaken on a term contract.

    The most essential elements of cost recording are that:

- The method used must be simple and understandable.
- Analysis must be regular and frequent, monthly or weekly as appropriate.
- Actual cost must be compared with the estimated cost.
- Cost recording must be viewed as an essential element in 'managing' cost.
- There must be mechanisms available to action problems when they are identified.
- The method should appreciate cash flow and variances to cost within its procedure, where appropriate.

The main tasks of cost control, applicable to both client and contractor, can be summarised as follows:

(i) *Non-recurring tasks*
- Development of a policy statement on cost.
- Preparation of the forecast of expenditure (budget).
- Classification of cost breakdown, (by cost range, work type, location, etc.).
- Agreement on the management strategy towards cash flow, variances and cost recording.

(ii) *Recurring tasks (half yearly)*
- Updating and revising budget and cash flow forecast.
- Updating profit appraisal from revised cash flow forecast.

(iii) *Recurring tasks (monthly)*
- Updating short term cost plan and cash flow forecast and relate to budget.
- Measure and value all works completed.
- Complete interim valuations, where appropriate.
- Assess any cost liabilities (unpaid contractors, suppliers, etc.).
- Determine the effects of monthly evaluation upon the half yearly budget.

(iv) *Recurring tasks (weekly)*
- Measure works in progress continuously.
- Value works completed.
- Update short term plan if vital to the next week's work, otherwise leave to monthly evaluation.

Table 6.5 *Estimated cost assessment for small works on annual term contract.*

Estimated small works expenditure (Annual contract)

Small works job	Start	Finish	Estimated cost £	Labour £	Plant £	Materials £	Overheads £
Machine bases	Jan	Mar	5000	3000	750	1000	250
Plinths	Feb	Feb	4000	2100	1200	500	200
Pipe racks	Jan	Apr	7000	4400	1250	1000	350
Sub-station	Jan	May	12 000	8000	1400	2000	600

Table 6.6   *Actual cost assessment for small works on an annual term contract*

Actual small works expenditure (Annual contract)

Small works job	Start	Finish	Actual cost £	Labour £	Plant £	Materials £	Overheads £	Variation £	%
Machine bases	Jan	Mar	4700	2700	750	1000	250	300	6%
Plinths	Feb	Feb	3900	2100	1100	500	200	100	2½%
Pipe racks	Feb	May	7250	4600	1250	1000	400	-250	-3½%
Sub-station	Jan	May	11 600	8000	1400	1600	600	400	3%

Cost modelling

In recent years, for more extensive small works, such as those undertaken on a term contract basis or lump sum basis, cost modelling has become a useful management tool to assist cost planning and control. An effective cost model depends for its success upon an accurate and realistic model of the pattern of small works and the precise application of how cost is apportioned to the various elements of the works. The difficulty with small works is that, even on a term contract, the nature and volume of the work is virtually unknown before the work is undertaken and therefore, an accurate model is difficult to produce. Where a pattern can be anticipated by a more knowledgeable and experienced client, a suitable model makes cost control easier to implement.

Cost modelling lends itself to computing applications and accurate predictions of the effect of changes to the work may be made. An important factor in cost modelling is its propensity for presenting a clearer understanding of the consequences of a manager's decision upon the work and also gives a clearer indication of the risk and uncertainty involved with the work.

The accuracy of cost modelling depends upon the interaction of cost with time, quantity and quality and the various costs must be clearly defined and appreciated, these include;

(i) *Fixed costs* – those which are incurred, irrespective of the type or volume of work undertaken.

(ii) *Time related (running costs)* – those which are incurred in, for example, the use of plant items during the undertaking of the works.

(iii) *Quantity related costs* – those which are incurred when using, say, materials which will obviously vary with the amount of work undertaken and amount of resources used.

While the fixed costs include direct and indirect costs which do not vary as the works are undertaken, time related and quantity related costs do and it is these variable costs which are difficult to allow for within any cost model. Where it is possible to model their variance, their effect upon the overall cost pattern is useful information in the more effective control of cost for small works organisation and management.

6.4   Control of quality

General

The control of quality is the third crucial aspect of organisation and management for small works. Control of quality may be considered in two main categories; the control of:

(i) *'Quality' of the work* – (*workmanship*) this involves: ensuring that the attributes of the work, be it building or structure, satisfies the specified needs; measuring, where possible, the ongoing and finished works against recognised standards; and implementing where appropriate, quality control and quality assurance procedures.
(ii) *'Performance' of the workforce* – this involves: assessment of the effectiveness of the work methods used and developing a means of measurement so that actual work can be assessed against that envisaged, sometimes referred to as 'measure of productivity' (see Figure 6.7).

Control of quality

The control of quality must surely be one of the most contentious issues in the organisation and management of, not just small works but, construction generally. Whilst there is increasing support for the use of independently recognised quality assurance systems within construction, based upon the framework of BS 5750: Quality Systems, the UK's national standard for quality assurance, quality control for small works surrounds the wholly practical supervisory function of inspecting work during construction and upon completion to ensure that the materials used and standards of workmanship are appropriate to the predetermined requirements.

It is not the intention of this book to review in detail the extremely searching and, at times, ambiguous nature of quality, quality control and quality assurance, these are areas which have merited publications in their own right. Rather, it is the intention to provide an insight into the practical aspects of quality control as an important management and supervising function, as this is directly pertinent to its application to small building

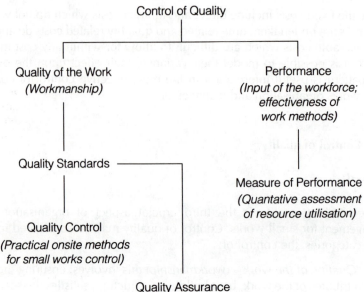

Figure 6.7   An overview of the process of quality control for small works

works. The role of quality assurance is explored at a basic level since its application is useful to clients procuring small works under term contracts or lump sum contractual arrangements.

Definitions
As there is frequently considerable confusion between the aims of quality control and quality assurance and where and when their principles should be applied, it is pertinent to define a number of the issues involved.

Quality may be defined as:
The totality of features and characteristics of a product or service that bear upon its ability to satisfy a given need[2] (BS 4778).

Quality control may be defined as:
The essential techniques and activities that sustain the product or service quality to specified requirements (BS 4778).

Quality assurance may be defined as:
All activities and functions concerned with the attainment of quality (BS 4778).

Or, in more practical terms:

'An objective demonstration of the builder's ability to produce building work in a cost effective way to meet the customer's requirements.' (Chartered Institute of Building)[3].

Small works do not generally lend themselves to the principles and practices of quality assurance. The works are small, are not substantial in volume and last only for a short duration, relative to other construction projects. This should not infer however, that the principles are inapplicable, for some of the concepts are pertinent and certainly both the client and contractor can impart significant influence upon the achievement of quality.

Problems of achievement
The main reasons for failing to produce the required standards of quality in small works on-site are:

- A lack of understanding of the levels of quality required by the client.
- Poor definition in the roles, duties and responsibilities towards quality allocated to site managers, foremen and the workforce.
- Inadequately prescribed standards for quality.
- Ineffective quality control procedures used on site for inspection and, where necessary, testing.
- Inadequate standards of workmanship by the operatives.
- Ineffective first line supervision by foremen and chargehands at the workplace.
- Imbalance in the definition of project priorities with time and cost parameters outweighing the requirement for good performance and quality.

The aforementioned suggest that it is the contractor alone who assumes responsibility for the problems of achieving good quality. This is, in fact, far from true. The achievement of good quality depends equally upon the actions of the client and other parties involved in the undertaking of small works such as material suppliers and, where applicable, sub-contractors.

Client involvement
On a construction project, procured traditionally, the client is likely to appoint a design consultant, often an architect, who procures the services of the contractual parties and other inputs and who is responsible for overseeing all aspects of the project's organisation and management including the achievement of quality. On small building works, it is most unlikely that a design consultant will be employed, rather any design work will be carried out in-house, if the client has such a provision, or by placing reliance in the contractor to draft a suitable design solution to the client's basic brief and specification. Where the client takes no design initiative and relies upon the

contractor for the design and construction, the client can still play a part in the organisation and management of the works by:

- Selecting an appropriate contractor.
- Being 'involved' in the works throughout the total building process.
- Having clear ideas on the requirements and specification of the works.
- Clearly specifying to the contractor the levels of quality required.
- Monitoring construction progress with the contractor.
- Showing commitment to the achievement of quality in all aspects of the work.

In pursuing the achievement of good quality, even seeking to implement quality assurance procedures, it could be recommended that the client procures construction services only from a reputable building contractor whose organisation operates a registered quality assurance system with one of the recognised certification bodies. Within the sphere of small works however, it is a plain fact that only a very few contractors will have quality assurance certification and a client seeking to engage only quality assurance registered contractors, sub-contractors and suppliers would simply be unable to procure the work.

A high proportion of general and specialist building contractors are small companies with a minimal staff complement and the vast majority of small works will be undertaken by such contractors. Such companies are unlikely to have the necessary assets, time or personnel to sustain a formalised quality assurance system and, in any case, they are unlikely to be operating in a market sector where quality assurance is essential to their trading activity or commercial survival.

Suppliers and sub-contractors
The same criteria that may apply when a client selects a contractor may apply equally where the contractor chooses material suppliers and sub-contractors. Ideally the contractor should procure only from a reputable source that operates its own quality assurance system that complies with BS 5750 and is, for example, listed on a recognised listing such as the BSI Register of Firms of Assessed Capability. Again the number of sub-contractors and suppliers with certification or featuring on recognised published listings is limited. In small works management, the contractor will, almost exclusively,. procure locally based suppliers and sub-contractors and these are most unlikely to have any propensity for formalised quality assurance. Only those suppliers and sub-contractors who are part of a large national organisation are likely to present this potential. This aspect may be of little significance to the management of industrial, jobbing, small works but may be an important issue for the selection of services to extensive term contracts.

The contractor
The contractor can influence the achievement of quality at two main stages of the works, during the:

Pre-construction stage:
- Liaising with the client to determine the genuine requirements for the works.
- Reviewing, with the client, the drawings, specification and other control documents, if available, or, if the contractor is to design and specify for the works, to liaise with the client in their preparation.
- Discuss with the client the requirement for quality in relation to other project variables such as time and cost.

Construction stage:
- Provide a well structured and organised approach to work and site organisation.
- Assign operatives to the work with the requisite skills and experience.
- Clearly specify the requirements of the works to the workforce.
- Accurately monitor quality and performance on-site.
- Take immediate action to halt the work and rectify discrepancies as they occur.
- Liaise with the client constantly to review progress.
- Reward good quality work, not just work speedily carried out, i.e. make bonus incentive schemes quality related and not necessarily time related.
- Encourage high morale and self-achievement in the workforce.

Practical quality control
Practical quality control for small building works is essentially a supervisory function of the contractor's site management which can be considered under three main headings, each with a number of constituent parts. These are:

(i) *Creating a positive working environment* :
- By selecting the most appropriate operatives, in terms of skills and experience for the task.
- Ensuring that there are suitable working conditions and temporary facilities.
- Programming the work so that it may be carried out efficiently and effectively and with appropriate support from the organisation and the client.
- Arranging the work so that it is not affected by inclement weather, where possible.
- In conjunction with the client, allowing easy access for the workforce, plant and materials.

(ii) *Provision for clear instructions and communications:*

- Clearly specifying to the workforce the standards of quality expected both by management and the client.
- Providing clear and concise information for use at the workplace including drawings, specification and other control documentation.
- Discussing the work requirements not only with the foreman or charge-hand but with all the workforce.
- Identify, before work commences, those criteria by which the work will be assessed and deemed to be or not be acceptable.
- Providing a channel of feedback from operatives to management to discuss problems as they arise.

(iii) *Inspections during the works*

- Arrange regular management visits to the workplace to assess progress, discuss problems and difficulties.
- Meet with the client at the workplace to review the works regularly.
- Provision for unscheduled visits and random spot checks to monitor the workforce activities.
- Gather information in a systematic way for application to progressing and time control and cost evaluation.

Inspection is perhaps the most crucial aspect of small works quality control. Because small works are limited in nature and undertaken over such a short time span, relative to other construction works, inspection must be not only regular but considered a continuous activity. Ideally, inspections should be:

- Daily, or where the works are expected to have a longer duration inspections at two to three day intervals.
- At least one 'formal' technical visit weekly to assess, record and review progress with the workforce and the client.
- Scheduling to coincide with the more complex and difficult operations or critical stages in the progress of the works to provide guidance and support to the workforce.
- Timed to meet the relative degree of skill, experience and reliability of the workforce. Some operatives may require more or less supervision than others.
- Planned to coincide with the issue of any instructions so that new instructions or changes to the work can be discussed at the workplace.
- Scheduled to coincide with any visit made by the client to ensure that verbal instructions are not issued to the operatives without first referring to the contractor's site management.

Inspections of this nature will ensure that both the contractor and client is fully aware of the progress and quality standard of the works. They will be able to identify any variance to the programmed schedule or cost budget and take appropriate action to stabilise ongoing activity and also to ensure that work completed is in accordance with the requirements and instructions given. Any difficulty arising is likely to be dealt with speedily and long before the situation would be able to get out of hand, which would not be the case if inspections were irregular and at long intervals.

There will always be situations where close supervision and inspection is not possible, such as when working in remote locations. In such cases the contractor can simply only do his best and will be almost exclusively reliant upon the integrity, honesty and reliability of the workforce to undertake the work as efficiently and cost effectively as possible.

Quality assurance

Whilst virtually all small works building contractors are unlikely to be involved in registered quality assurance schemes, larger building, civil engineering and specialist contractors who operate on a national level and who undertake annual and term contracts for larger clients may be involved with quality assurance schemes.

Quality assurance is concerned with developing a formal structure, organisation and operational procedure to ensure good quality throughout the total building process. 'Quality' is generally defined as a measure of fitness for purpose in the sense of meeting the client's needs whilst 'assurance' derives from the assessment and recognition of a contractor's quality management system by an individual assessor or 'certification body'. Quality assurance develops an industry-wide framework within which individual organisations such as contractors can develop their own quality systems to the guidelines of BS 5750: Quality Systems, the national standard by which quality assurance systems are currently assessed.

Since quality assurance is an integral aspect of the total building process, its remit encompasses the stages of design, construction, and even maintenance and facilities management. Although small works, in general, do not undergo the same design process as more extensive construction projects, the quality assurance principles for construction site management and supervision are applicable, to some degree, to small works organisation and management. BS 5750 : Quality Systems, advocates systematic control of quality through documented procedures, continuous monitoring and practical feedback. Assessment of the system by certification gives the quality system external recognition. A BS 5750 : Quality System is generally explained as a management system with quality control as its basis and drawing heavily on inspection and verification. Development of quality systems has led to total quality management and initiates a framework for self-inspection with each construction team member assuming responsibility for quality. Whilst many within the construction industry have attempted to deride BS 5750 as inappropriate for construction applications, it can be applied successfully to all forms of building projects including small building works. Attention is therefore, drawn to Appendix 4 which provides sources of further information in connection with quality assurance.

Control of performance

Performance is concerned with two main aspects:

(i) The level of effectiveness of the work methods.
(ii) The input of the workforce.

These allow one to determine the effectiveness and efficiency of performance against which the actual work can be compared. Small works do not readily facilitate accurate measurement of performance as works may differ widely, they have a broad range of values and sizes and different construction methods may be used. These differences make precise definition and quantitative evaluation difficult. Essentially, a simple 'before and after' assessment is needed and although this approach may be considered somewhat rudimentary, it is paramount that any method used to assess performance be simple and intelligible to both management and the workforce. Performance measures are many and varied with some being simple, some complex, and certainly some more accurate than others.

Although the level of performance achieved is likely to be circumstantial to the client, it is useful in, for example, checking works order valuations and can assume great importance if direct labour is being evaluated. Performance measures are perhaps more pertinent to the contractor who will be greatly concerned with assessing the output of the operatives employed and also in evaluating the work methods used with the accent upon improving approach for higher work efficiency and greater cost effectiveness.

The following list, whilst not being exhaustive, does give some indication as to the types of performance measures used. Most approaches rely upon simple mathematical ratios although some depend upon wholly qualitative assessments. These methods include:

- *Number of orders completed*
  This is a very superficial assessment which essentially only reflects the numbers and values of work orders or daywork orders completed. Over a long period of assessment this method can provide some measure of work resources and approximate task duration for determining future work.
- *Manhour recording*
  Recording the actual expenditure on the works can provide some measure of assessment to aid the structuring of future works. The method is only useful where small works are undertaken on a regular

basis and where the size and value of the works are similar. Again, the method is superficial and has similar disadvantages to recording the number of works orders.

• *Material requisition*
Recording the quantity of material used may provide some indication of the amount of work completed. This method may record the total value of materials used over a long period or those used by individual work gangs on work sections. It is difficult however, to use this method effectively since small works may be more labour orientated than other construction work and the use of materials may give a false impression of the real work done.

• *Output per operative*
This provides a simple ratio of the cost of resources used against the number of operatives employed:

$$\frac{Total\ input\ of\ labour,\ plant,\ materials\ and\ overheads}{Number\ of\ operatives}$$

Such calculations do not appreciate overtime rates, trade gang distributions and take no account of the degree of difficulty experienced by the different trades in undertaking the work.

• *Actual against estimated task durations*
This is a more direct approach which compares actual manhour expenditure with that estimated for the work:

$$\frac{Estimated\ manhour\ expenditure\ on\ the\ works\ order}{Actual\ manhour\ expenditure\ on\ the\ works\ order}$$

This method does have a number of disadvantages in that it depends upon the accuracy of the estimate and also when compiling the estimate some aspects of the work may not be pre-measured due to its uncertain or even unknown nature. It also takes no account of trade skill difference or disparities between individual small works as it lumps all works together.

It may be more effective to give a 'standard hour' assessment so providing a more applicable and reliable comparison between actual and estimated expenditure by means of a performance factor:

Performance factor =
$$\frac{Standard\ time\ (in\ hours)\ for\ small\ work\ job}{Actual\ time\ (in\ hours)\ expended}$$

where 'standard time' or standard hour' is the amount of work that can be performed in one hour by a representative operative.

162

This measure can also be expressed in cost terms, as follows:

Cost per standard hour =
$$\frac{Total\ cost\ for\ small\ work\ job}{Standard\ time\ (hours)\ expended}$$

Implementation
All the performance measures described are essentially concerned with assessing the quantitative efficiency of the workforce and the minimisation of resources used. Evaluating the effectiveness of the work in achieving the client's objectives is a different matter which requires the contractor to consider the performance of the work in relation to quality, time and cost. It is therefore, necessary for the contractor to make both qualitative and quantitative assessment in the practical management of small works on site to continually ensure that the ongoing work meets with the project's objectives.

References

1   Griffith, A., *Quality Assurance in Building*, Macmillan Press (1990)
2   British Standards Institution, BS 4778: (1971)
3   Chartered Institute of Building, *Quality Assurance in Building* (1987)

7 Practice and Case Study Analysis

7.1 Current status of small building works management literature

There are few meaningful literary works addressing the procurement and management of small building works. The main thrust of interest is directed, in the main, towards the management of minor building and other construction projects or maintenance contracts. While some of the concepts are analogous with small works, other aspects have marginal relevance given the context in which small works is recognised in this book. The management of maintenance work draws closest comparison with small works as some of their intrinsic aspects display commonality in, for example, their size and complexity.

The well-known works of Milne[1], Lee[2], Chudley[3] and Seeley[4] for example, all address the procurement, management and execution of maintenance contracts, but a number of the main issues they highlight apply equally to the management of small building works. Such issues include the difficulties and problems surrounding: the argument between the client using direct labour or letting the work out to a contractor; the relationship between the client and the contractor; the type of procurement arrangement for the work; and the different organisations and management procedures which may be adopted.

The argument between client employment of direct labour or contracting the work is well appreciated by the aforementioned authors who concur that choice should always be based upon cost, time and quality, but equally upon the degree of convenience to the client, although the ultimate decision must always be based on the individual circumstances that prevails within the client organisation and within the constraints set by the commercial climate at the time the decision is to be made.

The relationship between the client and the contractor is explored by Milne who suggests that where a client regularly employs the same contractor the lack of competition can increase the cost of the work and quality also tends to suffer because of the inadequate practical supervision of the ongoing work. Milne warns that a long term client–contractor interaction can give rise to a detrimental relationship between the contractual parties and that this must be guarded against. This issue is a serious consideration given that small works may be undertaken on an annual or term contract basis over a prolonged period.

Lee reviews the practice of procuring small maintenance works using works orders and daywork order approaches which again, marks parallel-interest with small building works which are, as described in this book, frequently procured using these methods. Various issues are discussed by Lee including the prioritising of works and the content and detail of works order forms and their operating procedures, some of which are similar to those suggested for small building works procurement.

While the works of Lee and Milne discuss the procurement of minor maintenance contracts, some aspects of which share common ground with small building works and their management, neither develops the procurement concept to consider forms of contractual arrangement and the implications this may have on their undertaking. Both do, however, support the view that defined contracts are preferred to reduce contractual ambiguity although it is also recognised that some works simply cannot be handled in that way and that a more informal approach is needed. This draws close comparison with small building works management as many small works are procured without reference to formalised methods. Seeley[4] deals with the specification, measurement, pricing, tendering procedures, contract administration, planning, financing, execution and supervision of maintenance work.

7.2   Recent investigation

While it may be said that there is a dearth of literature and research material in the area of small building works management, a study by Campbell[5] is a welcome and most relevant exception. This work, *The Management and Procurement of Small Works* (1990), an unpublished Master's degree thesis, examines specifically the problems surrounding small building works from both the clients' and contractors' perspective.

Investigation

Through detailed interviews with a number of general and specialist small works building contractors, the general methods of procurement and management of small building works used by the client organisation, (*a large national private sector client body*), were examined to identify problem areas and consider how these might be avoided in the client's procurement of future small building works. This approach was expanded by a number of site-based case studies to supplement the findings and recommendations drawn from the study.

Although the research approach draws exclusively on the procurement of small building works in one geographic location and it is anticipated that there will be some differences in the procedure adopted by the client organisation in other locations, the work does, nonetheless, begin to shed some light on the typical problems and concerns that arise in the procurement and management of small building works. All the contractors were small independent organisations and all had worked for the client on a number of occasions, with the works procured using individual works order arrangements.

Investigation sought to question the following aspects:

(i)   The relationship between the client organisation and the contractor.
(ii) Use of and procedures for tendering.
(iii) Application of individual small works orders as the basis of procurement.
(iv) Supervision arrangements by the client and its effects upon the contractor's approach on-site.
(v)   The general financial arrangements for small works payment procedures.

A number of other questions were posed but these concern logistic and circumstantial information used to record details of the type of small works building contractors (see Figure 7.1).

Findings

- *Relationships between the client organisations and the contractor.*
  As the contractor had been employed by the client on previous

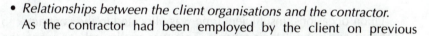

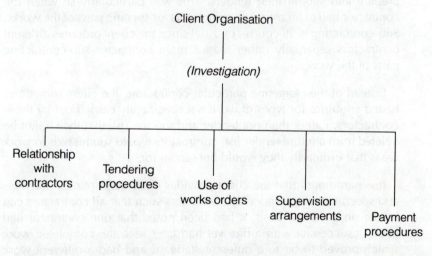

Figure 7.1   Areas of investigation, the management and procurement of small works[5]

occasions there had been an opportunity to build up a solid working relationship between the two parties. This ongoing relationship led to a number of points:

All the contractors suggested that a positive working relationship was fundamental to the success of the work. Some contractors saw distinct benefit in previous liaison since this gave a true perspective on the particular requirements expected by the client, in this case, for a clean and tidy approach coupled to high quality of workmanship.

The contractors also stated that it was advantageous that the client regularly lets the works out to tender. The regular opportunity to submit bids was perceived as a high motivator even though some contractors would be unsuccessful in securing work by this method.

The particular small works order form used by the client was well received as it specified a named individual responsible for arranging and overseeing the work. This 'personal' aspect was seen as a positive management step in generating closer collaboration between the client and contractor.

- *Use of and procedures for tendering.*
Whilst the contractors clearly favoured the use of open tendering allowing free competition for the client's work, a number of problems were identified, these were as follows:

Upon occasions, insufficient time was allocated to the contractor to prepare and submit their tenders. This was particularly so when the contractor had to arrange sub-contractors for specific parts of the works. Sub-contracting is, of course, unusual since the client procures different contractors separately rather than a main contractor sub-contracting parts of the work

Instead of then targeting particular contractors, the client sometimes issued enquiries for types of work not specifically carried out by those contractors. Rather than not tender and run the risk that they might be deleted from a future tender list, contractors would submit bids in work areas that ordinarily they would not tender for.

It is paramount that the client provides clear descriptions, drawings and specification to tendering contractors such that all contractors can tender on the same basis. It had been noted that one contractor had been unsuccessful with a bid, yet had later seen the completed work which proved to be to a different standard and had a different work content from that basis upon which the contractor had prepared his tender.

The financial level at which competitive and non-competitive bids were distinguished were thought to be too low. This notional limit is influential since, as seen in Chapter 4, even for small works the tender preparation cost is high as a proportion of the total cost. In this case, the contractor suggested that the limit be doubled to present a realistic differentiation between what would constitute a competitive situation and a non-competitive situation.

Little, if indeed any, information was being provided in the way of competitive tendering results. The contractors had no idea of the margin by which they were unsuccessful in their quotations and such information would be useful for their future tendering strategy.
ment.

- *Application of individual small works orders as the basis of procure-*
  Although most of the contractors readily accepted the client's small works order form approach, a number of contractors raised the following points:

  That the tendering form itself could be made simpler and therefore, more cost effective to both parties.

  Too much information was given in the way of drawings, specification and other control documentation in relation to the size of the jobs. This frequently complicated the issues involved and was felt unnecessary.

  Again, the competitive/non-competitive tendering differential was highlighted. Contractors suggested that a low limit meant considerable time was simply wasted in tendering for most jobs with a low intrinsic profit margin.

  To alleviate the difficulties presented by the competitive/non-competitive limit, the contractors suggested that the client might adopt a small works daywork order, a method used by other clients, to procure work when its requirements were difficult to specify or quantify. This would reduce the unnecessary tendering cost.

- *Supervision arrangements by the client and its effects upon the contractor's approach onsite*
  This question brought about the least favourable response from the contractors and a number of problems surrounding supervision onsite were identified, these being:

  The client was not always ready to allow the work to proceed when the contractors arrived on site and consequently, time was wasted at the start of the job.

Whilst the supervisory arrangements between the client and contractor were initially sound, it became apparent soon after commencement that the client's supervisor was not always onsite as and when required to allow the contractor easy access to workplaces and that when the client was in residence at a site there was still difficulty in providing easy and clear access to all aspects of the works. This lack of access was seen clearly to disrupt work continuity.

The client's supervisor was difficult to contact at times when problems arose and, as a consequence, work was unnecessarily held up awaiting client's instructions.

The client's supervisor was not always available to see and inspect work as it proceeded, but rather inspection became a retrospective activity.

It was suggested that the client's supervisor was insufficiently skilled in construction technology and management to properly oversee the work on site. This slowed up progress and often made decision making difficult.

- *The general financial arrangements for small works payment procedures.*
  The contractors' response to the financial aspect of small works appear mixed. Whilst some were quite satisfied with the client's financial arrangements, a number of others raised several issues, these being:

Contractors favoured the use of automatic transfer of payments using, for example Giro transfer, as this method gave the minimum of delay in receiving payment.

Some found too long a lapse between accounts rendered and receipt of payment and this presented a problem of severe cash flow for small contractors operating on a tight budget.

Payment was frequently found to be held up because some parts of the works were incomplete. This was further exacerbated where the work was delayed through no fault of the contractor. Contractors suggested interim payments should be made in such cases.

Payment to contractors was found to be held up within the client's financial system also. It was identified that this aspect could and should be alleviated by prompt accounting procedures within the overall client's organisation and management of small works.

The lack of client experience in construction activity was further explained, in particular with reference to supervision onsite. On the small works reviewed, it was suggested that quality standards and quality control should be afforded greater attention, as there was ample opportunity for the contractors to 'cut corners' and in so doing severely affected the quality of the works. Where the client had particular requirements for cleanliness, due to the proximity of equipment, it was suggested that the additional risk was often insufficiently stated to the contractor. By highlighting the risk more clearly, the contractor should be able to employ more able, suitable and experienced staff to meet the increased requirements. It was seen as essential that not only should clear descriptions of the work be given but also that information should be appropriate to the true requirements and not merely represent general instructions. It was observed that information of the wrong type was frequently provided, for example information describing workman-ship requirements rather than work content and specifications (see Figure 7.2).

The client suggested that many of the problems identified could be alleviated if the client had the propensity to give total supervisory coverage to every job but the large number of projects managed concurrently precluded this. The absence of client supervision at crucial points in the work's progress does, of course, mean that communication and control can suffer considerably. An interesting point made suggests that there was often some reluctance by the contractor to contact the client where problems arose, yet if the client was freely available on site there was a much greater willingness for consultation. Personal contact therefore, is seen as vital for effective management of small works on site.

Recommendations from the study

The main recommendations from the study can be summarised as follows:

- A formal daywork order should be used on very small jobs to provide a faster response mechanism to contractors when tendering. This would eliminate prolonged and costly tendering procedures and make useful time and financial savings for both the client and contractor. Although the client might pay more through 'marked-up' tenders, in both work order and daywork procurement this additional cost involved is likely to be offset by the shorter lead-time for procurement and through the reduced preparation of documentation.

- The financial limit for competitive tendering should be raised to alleviate many of the problems emanating from tendering for very small works. Similarly, a limit should be set on daywork orders, removing the need for contractors' quotations on very small works. It is still advocated however, that where competitive tendering is used, three, or more, quotations should be the norm to encourage a fair and genuine price to be determined.

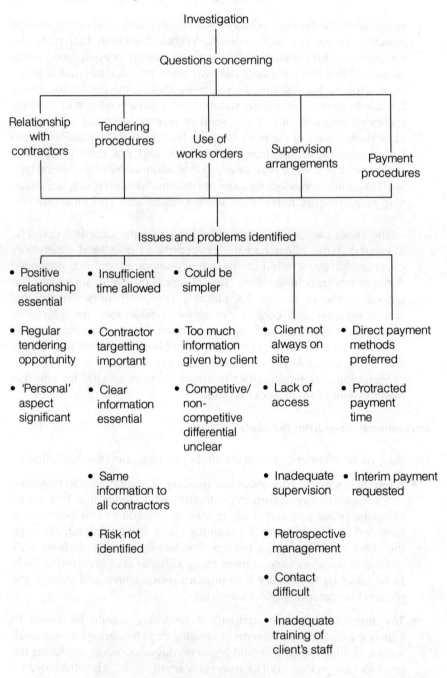

Figure 7.2   Findings of investigation on the management and procurement of small works[5]

- The need for additional training of client's staff was suggested since inadequacies in construction orientated experience was seen as one of the main reasons for lacking skills and supervision onsite. It was the absence of supervision that gave rise to repeated problems, in particular those associated with quality and performance.

Case study material revealed that it was often the case that the contractor paid little attention to the predetermined commencement dates for the works and that problems, when arising, were not effectively remedied. Again, problems which could be alleviated by better trained and appropriately skilled staff were left unattended or unresolved. It clearly highlights the importance to the client of deploying site supervision with the right skills and attributes and also the efficacy of not over-stretching supervisory resources too thinly so as to provide regular and ongoing organisation and management of small works on site. These aspects will be discussed further, together with more detailed recommendations for the more efficient and effective organisation and management of small works in Chapter 8.

References

1 Milne, R.D., *Building Estate Maintenance Administration*, Spon (1985)
2 Lee, R., *Building Maintenance Management*, Granada (1987)
3 Chudley, R., *Maintenance and Adaptation of Buildings*, Longman (1981)
4 Seeley, I.H., *Building Maintenance*, Macmillan Press (1987)
5 Campbell, C.W., *The Management and Procurement of Small Works*, MSc Degree Thesis, Heriot-Watt University, (un-published), (1990)

8 Management for Improvement

8.1 Difficulties and problems faced by management

The difficulties and problems which singly or in combination greatly influence the procurement, organisation and management of small building works can be generally grouped under three broad headings:

(i) Those presented specifically by the construction sectors, markets and business environment in which both clients and building contractors must operate.
(ii) Those deriving from a client's approach.
(iii) Those originating from a contractor's approach.

The difficulties and problems that occur within these three broad groups can be regrouped more appropriately under six headings, each of which represents a distinct phase in the process of small building works management, these being:

(i) Pre-procurement
(ii) Procurement
(iii) Commencement
(iv) Contract organisation and management
(v) Measurement and payment
(vi) Completion

8.2 Pre-procurement phase

The basis for success in procurement, organisation and management of small building works will originate before the client or contractor ever set foot on site. It was identified in Chapter 3 that a client who seeks to procure any small building work has to consider a great many issues. Some of these fall outside the client's organisation whilst some are fundamental aspects for decisions making within the client's organisation. The client will, obviously, require a building or structure which will meet the specific client requirements, that is true of any construction project and also, like any construction project, difficulty may arise since:

- The client may not know precisely what the requirements are.
- The client may not accurately reflect the needs in the brief.
- The client may perceive the requirements differently to the contractor.
- There may be discrepancies between what is expected or anticipated and what is actually achieved.

These problems are considerations for any construction project, but a number of specific issues relate particularly to small building works at the pre-procurement phase:

- Client's inability to identify true requirements of the work in the context of small building works; the client may have particular difficulty in identifying exactly what the project requirements are since small building works do not always use a 'traditional' (separate consultant) approach. Small works do not tend, for example, to utilise a specialised design input but rely upon, perhaps, a non-construction member of the client's staff for design input or, more likely, to rely upon the contractor to undertake the design as well as the construction. Notional ideas of the work by the client when procuring the contract may turn into something not intended nor really needed by the client. Over-design is one example of this where the contractor gives the client more than is actually needed to fulfil the basic function of the idea. It is more cost effective in the long term for the client to acquire specialist design guidance than rely upon guesswork or contractors' designs although this must always be determined in the light of the circumstances prevailing.
- Client may not appreciate the true cost implications of contracting out work: the client has a choice to make between contracting out work or using direct labour. Often, this decision is inherently determined by the nature of the client organisation but when choice is a factor the client often demonstrates an inability to accurately determine which would be more cost effective. The results may be that in-house labour is used when, in fact, it is far from cost effective and where the skills of the labour force may really be inappropriate to the work.
- Inadequate choice of procurement approach, documentation and control: it has been clearly identified that small building works are frequently procured on an *ad hoc* basis. Some clients are not sure of or choose to simply ignore the range of procurement, documentation and control mechanisms available to them. The client must appraise himself of the alternatives to satisfy four specific issues:
  (i) Appropriate adoption of method, procedure and documentation to procure and organise the work, and thereafter appropriate management approach to control the ongoing work.
  (ii) Appropriate form of contract to establish the interrelationship between the client and contractor to determine their respective responsibilities.

(iii) Appropriate selection of measurement and financial control technique, choice of schedule (where applicable), and payment procedures.

(iv) Appropriate selection of the contractor to best meet the needs of the work, and choice of other specialist inputs such as designer and quantity surveyor (where appropriate).

8.3 Procurement

The procedure used by the client for tendering small building works gives rise to, perhaps, more issues, difficulties and problems than any other phase in the small building works process. A number of difficulties were identified and described in Chapter 7, these were as follows:

- Lack of targeting tenders by the client creates tendering indecision for the contractor. Contractors waste time and money in tendering for work they are not suited for nor may want to undertake.
- Client often allows insufficient time for the contractor to complete a comprehensive and accurate tender, particularly where quotations for specialist materials must be obtained or where the necessity arises for sub-contractors to be employed must be addressed.
- Insufficient distinction made by the client between letting work out on a competitive basis and a non-competitive basis leads to contractors having to tender for small jobs with low profit margins. This, in real terms, is not cost effective for both the client and contractor.
- Clear description of the work must be provided to all prospective tenderers such that they all make their bids on the same basis. In addition, too much job information is found to be equally as prohibitive as too little information so, specifically, project information must be commensurate with the work.
- It can be difficult for the client to determine the validity of a tender and what constitutes a realistic bid. Tenders can be marked-up or down easily to the advantage of the contractor and once on the contract there can be manipulation of the system to the client's detriment.
- Little or no information is passed back to tenderers concerning the bids submitted but rejected. Although the client does not have to reveal such information, as the whole process of small building works is so often based on goodwill, feedback could only serve to encourage better relations across the tendering process.
- Restrictive tendering can set the scene for disharmony between the client and contractor: the decision by clients to tender their work openly is important to contractors. It was seen in Chapter 7 that contractors need to feel they have a chance of obtaining work and although in competition where many will fail to secure a particular

contract, morale is higher when at least they are allowed to tender rather than simply being left off the tender list. Open tendering also allows any sense of client favouritism to be dispelled.

- Selective tendering can create complacency: a client's view of selective tendering is that there may be cost savings from limiting paperwork and laborious procedures but the other side of the coin is that the client can become locked into a system where cost effectiveness can simply not occur as a result of his own complacency and also the complacency of the contractor who regularly tenders. To avoid any possibility of over-estimation or cost rigging, the client should always adopt rotational tendering from a selective but sufficiently broad list of contractors. This will go someway to safeguarding the client's interest whilst allowing regular opportunity for tender to a large number of contractors.
- Client's estimates of work values are often inaccurate: where small building works are to be carried out on an individual basis using a works order it is essential for the client to have a 'realistic' appreciation of the nature, complexity and value of the work. Often the client's perception of value is inconsistent with that of the contractor. On term contracts where an estimated annual value (EAV) is quoted, this must be realistic and accurate since tenders will be based fundamentally upon the value. Inaccurately specified values is one of the main contributors to determination of term contracts by contractors.

8.4 Commencement

The following problems are recognised as commonplace at the start of many small building works:

- Client is insufficiently prepared for the contractor's commencement on site: it was identified in Chapter 7 that the client is often simply ill-prepared for the contractor's arrival on site. It is commonplace for the contractor to arrive at the designated workplace only to find that access is unobtainable or denied to him. This aspect is further exacerbated where the workplace is remote from the organisation and management of both the client and contractor. Once the work has been ordered, it must be followed up by both parties to ensure that a representative from each is present at the date and time of start on site. Not only will this allow access and direction to the workplace but any queries relating to the work nature, method and location can be speedily answered, allowing the workforce to proceed efficiently. Often the contractor is left to find the workplace himself and construe from the drawings and specifications just what is actually required.

  It is not surprising then, that misinterpretation and problems occur. It is essential that the client's supervisor is present at commencement, perhaps more so than at any other time in the work process. It also serves another vital aspect of small building works management, that of bringing a 'personal' aspect to the work so that the contractor can associate the client organisation with the supervisor onsite. It was seen in Chapter 7 how the contractor's supervisor and workforce relate better to a client supervisor present on site than conversing over a telephone to discuss project difficulties.

- There is frequently a lack of easy access to the workplace for the contractor: some conditions of contract for small building works state that the client's supervisor is responsible for arranging access to the workplace and if this is obstructed then the contractor may be able to recover additional costs for non-productive time incurred. In practice, the contractor usually has to arrange for access to the workplace, usually in liaison with the client organisation. Arranging access may be more difficult than one might imagine, particularly if the work is in a remote location, at an unoccupied client facility or in a particularly sensitive or hazardous site. Even in occupied premises it may not be as simple as knocking at the door, especially if there is likely to be considerable disruption to the occupants because of the specific working procedures. The client must make someone clearly responsible for controlling access to the workplace on an ongoing basis, both to avoid disruption to the client and to avoid discontinuity for the contractor.

- Client does not always ensure that the contractor commences work on time as per order, instructions and agreed conditions: case study material, presented in Chapter 7, highlighted that frequently a contractor pays little attention to the predetermined commencement date and time and moreover that the client does not chase up the contractor expeditiously. Certainly, when a customer procures a craft operative for a minor jobbing work, there is often considerable leeway extended before the customer will actually complain. Of course, in the jobbing work situation there is unlikely to be any enforceable agreement but for other works there may be remedies for such instances. In practice though, this type of problem goes hand in hand with that of client supervision at commencement. The client should agree to meet the contractor at the designated place and on time to ensure that work is commenced as agreed. Should the contractor not appear, the client must investigate immediately to ascertain the reason for the delay since any procrastination by the contractor could have cost implications for the client. This is, obviously, the reverse situation to the client not turning up to allow access at commencement. Again, effective communication between the parties is the key to expeditious commencement.

8.5   Contract organisation and management

It is fundamentally clear that the onsite organisation and management of small building works is no less important than that required for any other construction project. In the past there has been a tendency for both clients and contractors to view small building works as, perhaps, the poor relation of new building work such that they have not received the due recognition they deserve and have not received the organisation and management input generally required to give small building works the opportunity for optimum success. A number of distinct difficulties and problems can be traced back to attitude and approach:

- Inadequate working relationship between client and contractor: there can be little doubt that small building works rely, perhaps more so than other projects, upon the honesty, integrity and goodwill of the contractual parties because of the nature of the methods used to organise and manage the work. It is not surprising therefore that it was identified in Chapter 7 that a positive and integrative working relationship is vital to the success of the works. The difficulties of the client not being on site at commencement and when key issues arose and the contractor failing to start on time were all problems originating from the basic lack of integration between the client's and contractor's organisations. It is paramount therefore, that the client and contractor appoint a named individual to oversee their respective activities and that interrelations become a continuous dialogue and not just communication when problems arise or when decisions need to be taken. The ground work for this, of course, must be covered before the work ever reaches the onsite phase.
- Volume of individual works orders can create ordering complexity: it was mentioned earlier that, for example, on term contracts, the sheer volume of orders can create complexity in what should be a simple management procedure. It is essential to keep the ordering method simple, clear and concise to minimise the paperwork and procedures generated, such that management spends less time on bureaucracy and more time on the actual organisation and management of the works.
- Client's supervisor is difficult to contact and not always available quickly: frequently the client's supervisor or works superintendent is difficult to contact as work proceeds, with the likely result that where problems arise work is held up awaiting instructions or advice. Realistically, the client's supervisor cannot be available at all times for the work may be remote or other pressures simply preclude constant attendance. Supervisors must be available however at key points in the construction phase, be it for providing information, answering technical queries or inspecting and approving work. Procedures must be adopted

such that the client visits the site regularly in conjunction with the contractor. In addition, the client should make someone available to liaise with the contractor by telephone so that the client is freely available to address those unexpected situations which frequently arise in the course of all construction works.

- Inadequate training and experience of client's supervisors: unlike other construction work, small building works are often managed by the client's own staff and by persons who have little or no training in construction activities. For example, the supervisor may be a pro-duction supervisor of a chemical plant or manufacturing organisation who, while understanding the nature of the requirement for the finished product, may not appreciate the intricacies of the building method, procedures and management. The implications for the client in not providing an appropriate supervisor is likely to be slow or poor decision making, slow progress and the general lack of control of the works. The client must appoint trained and experienced supervisors in the field of the work and these persons should be sufficiently endowed with the ability and empowered to make decisions on behalf of the client organisation. Similarly, the contractor must appoint reliable staff and operatives as small building works frequently necessitate working without constant supervision.
- Imbalance between time, cost and quality: like all construction to some extent, the practical compromise between the three main project variables, time, cost and quality means that quality and performance of the works is treated disproportionately to time and cost. Because of the nature of small building works, more so than on other projects, the poor control of progress and budget can quickly lead to excessive imbalance such that any propensity for achieving value for money and good quality is almost instantly lost. The short duration of a small works job means that there is simply no opportunity to claw back lost time and resources as one might be able to do on other construction projects. When fixed priced work is involved, effects may be minimised but when work is carried out on a daywork basis, time and costs quickly mount up and even where good quality is achieved the chances are it will not, in financial terms, represent good value for money. The client must therefore, know what he wants, control activity and expenditure closely and be realistic about the interaction between time, cost and quality.
- Retrospective rather than active management is frequently adopted: there is simply no substitute for good supervision; it is vital. Due to the attitudes towards small building works previously mentioned there has been a tendency to undervalue supervision and management. This is ill-founded because, quite simply, the overall spend on small works is often higher than on new build work, in particular on term contracts, and the need to supervise, inspect and approve work is just as relevant

for small works as for larger projects. Regular resource planning and progress meetings are essential and these should bring the client and contractor together more frequently than for other types of projects given that the duration of small building works is generally short. Weekly or fortnightly meetings should be considered on individual works orders and on a monthly basis for term contracts. It is essential that the onsite supervision is simple and while some documentation may be necessary, paperwork should be kept to a minimum to avoid becoming over-bureaucratic in nature.

Supervision must be active rather than passive and ongoing rather than retrospective. The client should always be available to see and inspect the work as it proceeds and not make inspection a retrospective and procedural event. Too many clients and contractors involved in small building works attempt to manage at a distance and, more so than most other projects, these works require 'supervision at the workplace' since the parameters for cost effectiveness and success are so much more narrow and restrictive than for other construction work.

8.6   Measurement and payment

Under almost all construction contracts the client's representative is expected to certify on a regular basis, normally at monthly intervals, the value of work satisfactorily completed by the contractor for that period. The valuation certificate issued by the client's representative, authorises the interim payment due to the contractor. A prerequisite to this simple and well accepted procedure is an efficient measurement, valuation and payment procedure. Inadequate procedures together with late payment has often been in the past and was rapidly becoming an ever greater problem within the construction industry in the early 1990s. As financial problems exacerbate so clients and contractors with cash flow problems retain the money they owe to other parties for as long as possible. In the same way that contractors suffer from late payment from clients so suppliers and subcontractors likewise suffer from late payment from contractors.

Whereas problems of this nature may be met head on through the strict procedures laid down in standard forms of building contract, small building works may not utilise such contractual forms effectively, leaving little or no propensity to mitigate such problems if and when they arise. In fact, the problem of late payment is far worse across the industry than one might expect because construction activity generally is plagued by non-standard forms of contract where procedures, apportionment of risk and available remedies to difficulties and problems are far from clear.

Small building works give rise to a number of distinct difficulties and problems in the phase of measurement and payment.

Measurement

- Volume of measurement is comparatively large for the small value of a works order: it may be impractical and uneconomic for the client to independently check and verify measurement for each and every order. There is therefore, a tendency towards self-measurement by the contractor, in particular on term contracts where the large number of orders makes client verification difficult, if not impossible. The client, although perhaps justifiably allowing self-measurement for reasons of practicality, must not become too reliant upon it and thereby become complacent. Rather, the client should seek to implement both onsite checks and valuation checks to those practices described and discussed in Chapter 6.
- Volume of separate works orders and daywork orders creates bureaucracy and excessive paperwork leading to verification difficulties and, in particular, auditing problems: the sheer volume of separate orders initiated by the client over a year, in particular under a term contract can be considerable. It is not surprising therefore, that difficulty continually exists in determining whether the client is: obtaining the expected level of quality in the works; is procuring the works in a cost effective way, either individual or in total; and is achieving value for money, probably the client's paramount concern. In conjunction with the aforementioned, the volume of orders cannot simply be minimised since this is governed by the amount of work to be undertaken. Rather the ordering system must be kept as simple as possible or the volume of paperwork becomes detrimentally overwhelming. Verification of ordering procedures must be conducted continuously as part of the ongoing management process. Auditing which is, essentially, a retrospective control and feedback mechanism is really inadequate in small building works management. The volume of separate orders and the high value of annual expenditure on individual or term orders can make auditing a nightmare. The cost of audit may even exceed any overpayment that is incurred through inefficient ordering procedures. Ongoing and active measurement and verification is however recommended and a number of fundamental questions need to be asked, for example:

  - how many checks should be made.
  - to what level of detail should the checks be carried out.
  - when shall verification be undertaken.
  - who should carry out the checks.
  - what methods should be employed.
  - what action is available when inconsistencies are apparent.

Again, the concepts and procedures underlying these questions are discussed in Chapter 6. Essentially, the answer, in short, comes down to one of good client supervision and management. Although client managerial controls are essential, care must be taken not to over-impose on supervisory staff with red tape and paperwork at the expense of their primary function, onsite supervision and management.

- Responsibility for measurement is frequently unclear and poorly established: the responsibility for measurement must be established. The client does not always employ a quantity surveyor to handle financial aspects but rather relies upon technical and supervisory staff to double up in this capacity. Alternatively, the client often adopts a self-measurement approach where the contractor will self-measure and value orders up to a predetermined limit. In either case, the client must take steps to verify the efficacy of the process used. Larger contracts, such as term arrangements, will, of course, employ joint measurement by the client's quantity surveyor and contractor's quantity surveyor but even in this case some clients expect the contractor to self-measure orders up to a set value. Bearing in mind that checks must be effected somewhere in the process, the savings made from omitting client measurement is probably outweighed in the additional cost of checking the contractor's valuation. It is likely that joint measurement would be the most cost effective in the long term. For individual orders however, the client and contractor, through necessity, may not employ elaborate measurement and valuations techniques as this would be simply too cost prohibitive. Rather, the process is reliant upon the diligence, honesty and integrity of the contractor's foreman or supervisor to accurately measure and value the work and upon the fairness of the client in agreeing the account. Small building works do, without doubt, rely heavily upon a firm but fair approach by the client and contractor and therefore goodwill goes a long way towards project success.
- There is some potential, however small, that measurement and valuation will be subject to error and malpractice.

  It is essential to comment that the degree of error and level of malpractice in small building works management is probably no more excessive than that of any construction project, but nonetheless such things do occur and management should therefore, employ both preventive and detective procedures. There have been documented cases of corruption and conspiracy to defraud but these are seen, to be positive, as isolated incidents. More often than not, problems such as error in measurement and valuation occur through the parties being over-cautious in their approach rather than any intent to seriously cheat each other. As discussed in Chapter 4, the most common difficulties encountered are:

  – for works procured individually on measured rates, the possibility that the contractor's bid will be over-priced or marked up.

- for daywork orders, that the contractor's claim for labour, plant and materials will be over-stated
- for term contracts, that inaccurate measurement and valuation will, again, lead to over-payment by the client.

It is clearly evident that these aspects rely heavily upon the honesty of the contractor and upon the supervision of the client. It is however, not enough for the client to simply trust the contractor but must rather employ checks to ensure that the client's interests are consistently safeguarded. Such issues are discussed in Chapters 5 and 6.

Payment

- Late payment can have catastrophic effects upon small building organisations: late payment is fast becoming one of the industry's most prominent and vexed issues. More and more building firms, manufacturers, material suppliers and smaller sub-contract organisations are simply going out of business as clients with cash flow problems hold on to the money they owe for as long as possible. Small building works contractors are clearly more prone to this difficulty than other building organisations. Most small contractors will function and exist on a tight operating budget where cash flow is crucial to their day-to-day survival. There is little doubt that there is frequently a long lapse between accounts rendered and receipt of payment. This tends to occur in small works more so than other spheres of building, since small works may not utilise standard contracts within which payment is governed by contractual entitlement.

    Problems with measurement may be the first sign that payment will be problematical. There is, after all, little incentive for the client to rush measurement and prompt the contractor and more than likely a self-measurement process will throw the onus upon the contractor to make payment valuation of the work completed. Once in the system, it is not uncommon to find there is some procrastination and bureaucracy whilst the paperwork is handled and accounting and payment procedures deployed. It is often the combination of these aspects which retards the speedy discharge of payment.

    Early indications of problems may be seen by the contractor in the slow verification of interim valuation and generally late process of the account from site to office for example. In practice, these are issues that the contractor should address quickly and simply not allow to happen. Small works are, by nature, small and their short duration should be commensurate with prompt and efficient payment by the client. Regular monitoring by the contractor is recommended. On term contract financial management is generally separated from onsite management but when a small job is procured, onsite management, measurement and valuation may come within the remit of one individual. Irrespective of approach payment should be prompt, as there is nothing worse than late payment for discouraging the contractor to proceed expeditiously with the continuing works.

Some clients do, of course, use effective systems, a simple example being the use of automatic transfer payments such as Giro transfer. Such systems are favoured since, for while some delay is perhaps inevitable in the payment process, they do, in general, speed up the total process. The knock-on effect of payment problems for the contractor are that the contractor may not be able to take advantage of generous discounts for speedy payment with larger material suppliers and plant hire companies or may not be able to effect interest repayment on loans and overdrafts, all of which are crucial issues to the craft operative or smaller building contractor.

- There is often no facility for interim payment: while standard forms of building contract determine payment to the contractor in clear terms, small building works, particularly when procured individually on works orders, have no mechanism for interim payment. Payment is likely to follow successful completion of the work, irrespective of its duration. Of course, many small works are of short duration but some may take time to complete and without interim payment facilities cash flow soon becomes a concern for the contractor. It is, therefore, always advisable for an interim payment mechanism to be agreed before work commences. This will ensure that some advance on final payment is made, even if this is a calculation based on approximate percentage of work complete and is subject to final measurement, to maintain the contractor's working cash flow.

- Late agreement of final payment and outstanding money due to the contractor affect cash flow and continuity planning for future works: with most arrangements for small building works, even under a term contract, there is likely to be no agreement for liquidated or ascertained damages, although there is usually a predetermined defects liability period without retention. On a work basis which relies upon continual harmony and goodwill between client and contractor there may be little need for such devices since it is clearly in the contractor's interest to rectify any deficiency or defect that occurs. The client does, however, usually have the right to deduct monies from sums due for other works if the contractor fails to carry out remedial works. Where there is non-compliance with client's instructions the client may deduct a sum from the contractor to finance an arrangement with another contractor to complete the work. Certainly, the client should always seek to safeguard his position by such an inclusion in any agreement.

However, non-compliance may not always be the contractor's fault so the client must ensure that wrongful non-payment does not occur as determination may result. It is important, from a working perspective, for the contractor to rectify defective work quickly, notifying the client as work proceeds and for the client to recognise this action and reward compliance with rapid payment of any outstanding monies.

8.7   Completion

There are two main issues concerning the completion phase of small building works:

   (i) The criteria establishing the constitution of completion.
   (ii) Problems following completion such as remedial action on defective work.

With the former issue, problems can generally be traced back to the issue of the order itself. There must be a clearly agreed completion date specified on the order. Too often the parties verbally agree the expected completion date and leeway is then generally allowed surrounding the date. This can lead, over time, to a complacent relationship between the parties. The client must determine when the work is to be completed, monitor and approve its completion and issue a completion certificate on or before the predetermined date. The date is important because this signifies when the measurement and valuation phase commences. If work is prolonged the chances are it is costing the client money and making the job non-cost effective.

Although most small works, term contracts excepted, do not adopt a formal liquidated damages clause or use retention, most contractors would expect some defects liability rule to be included in any agreement with the client. If the job is a one-off there would be a chance that the contractor may not return to put right any defective work once the contractor had vacated the site. Final payment therefore, should always be withheld until the client is satisfied that the work is to his satisfaction. One of the most contentious issues within small works management is the client's inability to get the contractor to return to site to rectify defects if full payment has been made and no defects liability period was agreed. In such circumstances the client really has little if indeed any practical remedy.

8.8   Essential considerations and client's checklist

This section is divided into two parts. The latter is concerned with those general considerations of the client at each main phase of procurement and management of small building works, whilst the former part highlights those aspects which must be considered in relation to a particular category of small building works.

Specific considerations

Three categories are pertinent, these are:

(i) Small building works procured on a jobbing basis.
(ii) Small building works procured on an individual order basis.
(iii) Small building works procured under a standard form of contract, such as a term agreement or small/minor building project basis.

Small building works procured on a jobbing basis
Building work should be procured on a jobbing basis only when:

- The work is of a very low cost value.
- The low value makes tendering cost prohibitive.
- There is little risk incurred in making a verbal agreement.
- It is possible to procure the work without comprehensive documentation.
- A jobbing approach is the only practical method.
- More elaborate procurement is prohibited.

When adopting a jobbing works approach, the client should ensure that:

- The requirements for the work are clearly determined.
- At least three quotations (albeit verbal quotes over the telephone or on a site visit) are obtained.
- The requirements are clearly specified to the craft operative/builder.
- The price for the work is agreed in advance.
- The client/customer/owner/occupier are present at the workplace at commencement and throughout the work process.
- The work is conducted to the satisfaction of the client/customer/owner/ occupier.
- Payment (usually in cash, although traceable payment is preferred) is made only when the work is completed satisfactorily.
- The craft operative/builder can be contacted should problems arise following completion.

Small building works procured on an individual ordered basis
Building work should be procured on a individual ordered basis when:

- The nature, scale and value of the work exceeds the criteria specified for jobbing works.
- There is sufficient work to justify a more structured procurement approach yet insufficient flow of work to demand a term agreement.

- A formal written agreement between the client and contractor is preferred.
- Drawings, specification and control documentation are available.
- Tendering is preferred method of obtaining competitive quotations, (although the contractor may be selected).

When adopting individual ordering of works, the client should ensure that:

- Ordering is always on an official order, (works order or daywork order, depending upon the agreed method of measurement, valuation and payment).
- The level of detail given on the works/daywork order should always include, as a minimum, the thirteen points listed and described in section 4.2 of Chapter 4.
- The aforementioned detail should always be accompanied by drawings, specification and all relevant information relating to the work and its location.
- The client should never rely on verbal orders or instructions and always follow up verbal communication with written documentation.
- The work should be let on a competitive basis, where appropriate, and a minimum of three quotations should be obtained.
- A tender evaluation should always be made. Cost must be considered in relation to availability, convenience and risk.
- There is ongoing dialogue before work commences.
- A supervisor is onsite at commencement to facilitate access and further develop a working relationship with the contractor.
- Work is monitored regularly and that both routine and spot checks are made.
- That measurements and valuations made by the contractor are verified by spot checks during work in progress and upon completion.
- There is provision for written confirmation of completion.
- Defective work is recorded, notified to the contractor and rectified expeditiously.
- Final payment is made only when all work is completed to the client's satisfaction.

Small building works procured under a standard shorter form of contract such as a term arrangement or small/minor building project basis
Building work should be procured on a term contract arrangement where:

- The client perceives an ongoing need for procuring small building works.
- There is sufficient workload to provide continuity and cost effectiveness.
- A continued and rapid response is required by the client.

- One contractor is able to meet all, or the best part of the general work requirements (specialist inputs can be procured separately).
- A formalised agreement determines the methods of approach, measurement, valuation and payment.

Building work should be procured on a small/minor building project basis where:

- The nature, scale and value of the work exceeds the criteria for procurement on a works order/daywork order basis.
- The nature, scale and value of the work is appropriate to the use of a standard but 'shorter' form of building contract.
- The work has, ostensibly, one-off characteristics.
- Procurement may be non-competitive or competitive in approach and may be variable or fixed price in nature.

When adopting these approaches the client should ensure that:

- The types of work to be carried out are clearly specified.
- The scope of the contract selected is clearly determined.
- All contract definitions are described: (contract, employer, contractor, location, contract period, and for term contracts: orders, schedule of rates, percentage adjustments, etc.).
- Name of the supervising officer (works superintendent) is given.
- Contract period, commencement/completion dates are specified.
- On term contracts, details for ordering the works are specific including start and completion dates for each order.
- All relevant statutory regulations with which the contractor must comply are clearly stated.
- Any resources to be provided by the client are known to the contractor.
- Arrangements for providing access to the site or property and times when access is needed are clearly identified.
- On term contracts, priorities for work are known to the contractor, i.e. routine, urgent, emergency.
- The expected value of the work is agreed, for example on term contracts, the estimated annual value (EAV) is determined, together with maximum/minimum value of orders.
- The method of measuring and valuing the works is prescribed, for example in term contracts, the schedule of rates must be agreed, together with measured work/daywork distributions.
- Arrangements for making payment at interim valuations and final accounts are determined.
- Arrangements for payment following certificate of completion are agreed.
- The defects liability period and arrangements for the contractor to comply are clearly determined.

- Specification for quality and workmanship is conveyed to the contractor.
- Method of disposal of spoil, debris and rubbish from the site is agreed.
- Liquidated damages liability for delayed completion is fully appreciated.
- There is provision for the determination of the contract by either party.
- There is adequate provision for insurance of the works against damage, damage to existing property and injury to persons.
- There is provision for arbitration in the event that difficulties arise.
- There is Value Added Tax provision.

General considerations

The client's approach to procurement and management of small building works may be summarised in six phases:

- i   Pre-tender requirements.
- ii   Tender invitation.
- iii Tender submission.
- iv   Tender evaluation.
- v   Contract management.
- vi   Post-completion.

Pre-tender requirements

The client's approach to tendering and the response of the contractor will, obviously, vary in content and detail depending upon the form of arrangement or contract used. In general, however, the client should seek to:

- Undertake a detailed feasibility study of the proposed works or, if applicable, a condition survey of existing works:
  This will allow the client to consider:

  - a macro view of the proposal.
  - detail of the works.
  - identify potential problems.
  - alternatives.
  - outline time, cost and quality parameters.
  - appointment of consultant inputs.

- Consider appointment of consultants where appropriate:
  The client must consult the necessary consultants, such as:

  - Architect.
  - Structural Engineer.
  - Quantity Surveyor.

  – Specialist Engineer.
  – Site Engineer/Survey specialist.
  – Interior Designer/ergonomic specialists.
  – Landscape Architects and Urban Designers.

While it will not always be appropriate to consult or approach all of the aforementioned, consideration must be given at an early stage to avoid delays later. For example, the client may have to determine the need and value of appointing a quantity surveyor relative to the nature, size, value and complexity of the works. Another example may be the consideration of employing a design consultant or whether design work should be completed in-house.

The client should appoint any design consultant and accept the risk for their employment. Where the contractor is requested to contribute to the design process the position of liability must be considered carefully. The watchword for the contractor is, let the client process the design.

- Consider relevant legislation:
  The client must always consult:

  – The Local Authority for Planning and Building Control requirements.
  – The applicable legislation controls at Government and Local Authority levels.

- Consider which form of arrangement or control is to be used: the recommendation of forms of control is usually a duty of the design consultant, where appointed. If no consultants are used the client must select a form of contract and method of employing the contractor in relation to the factors discussed in Chapters 4 and 5. This could be a simple exchange of letters, an official order or a standard shorter form of building contract.
- Consider the specification: the specification, a schedule of instructions to the contractor, should detail the method of construction and nature of materials and components to be used in the works. As discussed previously, the specification should follow a standard format, be clear, concise and assist, not hinder, the understanding of drawings and instructions.
  The client should seek to:

  – provide comprehensive and clear documentation.
  – present all work to a standard trade or work section format.
  – relate to national standards where possible.
  – break down complicated works into smaller, more understandable parts.
  – be simple and systematic.

- Consider Schedule of Rates: the client should consider the options available in association with the form of arrangement and contract. These are considered in Chapters 4 and 5.
- Consider Prime Cost and Provisional Sums: where these would be applicable in a form of contract, the client or appointed consultants, should anticipate their nature and extent to give notional advice on expected cost values.
- Consider contingencies: the client will usually consider a contingency sum as this will invariably be included by the contractor in the tender. Figures of between 5 per cent and 10 per cent are normal.
- Other items: other factors will need to be considered by the client, although they are likely to be determined by the contract, these are:

  - Liquidation damages.
  - Defect liability period.
  - Completion.
  - Insurances.
  - Measurement and payment.

- Select the contractor: the client should seek to appoint the contractor in consideration of the factors discussed in Chapter 3. It is useful, in summary, for the client to:

  - maintain a rotational list of prospective contractors.
  - know the contractors well.
  - keep a professional distance.
  - never employ the same contractor for ease and convenience.
  - do not choose the cheapest automatically.

The client must consider all of the above carefully and seriously if the client is to:

- Acquire a fair element of competition in tender submissions.
- Obtain a fair price for the work.
- Secure value for money.

Tender invitation

The client must decide upon:

- Planning for the works.
- Who will undertake the design.
- Which form of contract will be used.
- Documentation must be provided in the form of:

i For Works/Daywork Orders:
  – The Order
  – Applicable Schedule of Rates.
  – Specification.
  – Drawings.

ii For Term Contracts:
  – Term of Contract.
  – Area/location of works.
  – Description of works.
  – Schedule of Rates.
  – Approximate value of contract.
  – Ordering procedure.
  – Minimum/maximum order values (value bands).
  – Daywork.
  – Prioritising the works.
  – Measurement and valuation techniques.

iii For Lump Sum Contracts:
  – Contract.
  – Bill of Quantities.
  – Specification.
  – Drawings.

- What form the tender will take:
  – Negotiated.
  – Competitive.
  – Time period for tendering.
  – Schedules of rates to be used.

- The client should, ideally, interview the prospective contractors, in which case the client must:
  – interview all tenderers.
  – Ask same questions to each for fairness.
  – Allow opportunity for questions from contractors.
  – Ascertain all information regarding the contractors' capabilities to undertake the work.

Tender submission
The contractor's responses should be to undertake the following:

- Check the completeness and clarity of the documentation.
- Ascertain the requirement for design, if appropriate.
- Review the programme for the works.

- Identify resources provided by the client.
- Identify the client's supervision arrangements and personnel to be onsite.

For Works/Daywork Orders:

- review the client's (*employer's*) requirements contained on the order.

For term contracts:

- establish 'cost basis'. For cost plus contracts review the cost to which the contractor's tender percentage should be added. For an unpriced schedule, clearly appreciate the client's instructions for pricing the items of works. For priced schedules, ascertain the basis of the rates.

For lump sum contracts:

- check details as for any other tender submission.

Tender evaluation
The client should always evaluate the tender:

- Check date and time of receipt.
- Review qualification clauses specified by the contractor.
- Compile tender evaluation sheet.
- Consider announcement date/time following submission and review.
- Issue formal instructions to the successful contractor.

Contract management (onsite)
The client should ensure that:

- A representative is present at commencement.
- There are regular site visits.
- There are regular site meetings.
- The contractor's programme is updated and reviewed.
- Insurances are current and valid.
- Information is speedily conveyed.
- All instructions are confirmed in writing.
- Inspections are carried out.
- Consideration is given to extensions/claims, as appropriate.
- Completion certificates are issued expeditiously.
- Measurement is undertaken and valuations approved.
- Payment certificates are issued at interim periods.
- Defect schedules are initiated and monitored.
- Certificate of making good defects is issued appropriately.
- Final certificate for payment is issued.

Post-completion (feedback)

If it is at all possible, the client should try to ensure that there is feedback from the completed works. Such information is not just for the client's benefit but may assist the consultants and contractor in appreciating the implications of problems experienced with a view to avoiding the same problem in the future. The client must ensure that:

- An adequate monitoring system is operated.
- Records are formally made and stored.
- Feedback is analysed and reviewed.
- Information is passed back to consultants and other parties.
- What is learned is used in future projects.

Appendix 1: Typical Standard Forms for Small Building Works Procurement and Management

TENDER EVALUATION SHEET

Contract:	Nr 3 Acid Plant Maintenance & Minor Capital Projects (Term Contract)
Contract No:	AP/3/Term/92/3
EAV:	£140 000 – £150 000
Measured Work: Day work:	£120 000 £20 000
Commencement Date: Term:	1/1/92 3 years

Work Category	Approx Value £	R. Black (Building Contractor)		Robb & Sons (Building) Ltd		T. Redman Ltd (Engs & Builders)	
		% adjustment on schedule	value £	% adjustment on schedule	value £	% adjustment on schedule	value £
Measured	120 000	+5%	126 000	+ 7%	128 400	+ 9%	130 800
Daywork	20 000	+7%	21 400	+20%	24 000	+15%	23 800
			147 400		152 400		154 600

(Details in works order bands not applicable)

Tender Accepted: R. Black (Building Contractor)   Value: £147 400 (approx)

Signed *M. Roberts*   Date: 22nd October 1991

Figure 8.1   Client's (Employer's) small building works term contract evaluation sheet

ABC CHEMICAL INDUSTRIES plc Head Office: Grangetown Refinery Grangetown G47 74G	Works Order (Foreman's order) Nr: 25724
	Project/Contract Reference: Nr 3 Acid Plant
	Date of Issue: 4th January 1992
	Issued By: R. Smith (Works Superintendent)

| To: R. Black (Building Contractor)
         123, Redland Avenue
         Redland, Grangetown

         Tel: 094 712 87327 | From: R. Smith (Superintendent)
         D Jones (Supervisor
         Small Works)
         Nr 3 Acid Plant

         Tel: int 4144 |

All work to be completed by: 17/2/92

Item	Work Location	Description	Estimated cost £
1	Pipe Trench 4a	Cast concrete pipe supports, (24 nr) as per drawing AP/3/041/a	4200
		WORKS ORDER	
		TOTAL ESTIMATED COST	£4200

Figure 8.2   Typical small building works order (foreman's order)

ABC CHEMICAL INDUSTRIES plc Head Office: Grangetown Refinery Grangetown G47 74G	INSPECTION SHEET	
	Order Nr: 25724	Date of Issue: 4/1/92
	Project ref: Nr 3 Acid Plant	Completion Date: 17/2/92
	Inspector: D. Jones	Date of Inspection: 19/2/92
Contractor: R. Black (Bld Contractor)		Sheet No 1 (of 1)

Item	Description	Remarks
1	Pipe Trench 4a - Pipe Supports (drawings AP/3/041/a)	North - South run, supports 1 to 22 fully completed to drawings and specification Nr's 23 + 24 incomplete, bolt jigs not to specification (to be corrected by contractor and reinspected as soon as possible)

Figure 8.3   small building work inspection sheet

ABC CHEMICAL INDUSTRIES plc Head Office: Grangetown Refinery Grangetown G47 74G	Variation Order Nr: 1314
	Works Order Nr: 25724
	Date of Issue: 16/1/92
	Issued by: R. Smith (Works Superintendent)

To: R. Black (Building Contractor) 123, Redland Avenue Redland, Grangetown Tel: 094 712 87327	From: R. Smith (Superintendent) D. Jones (Supervisor Small Works) Nr 3 Acid Plant Tel: int 4144

All work to be completed by: 17/2/92

Item	Work Location	Description	Estimated cost £
1	Pipe Trench 4a Pipe Supports (drawing AP/3/041/a)	Alter dimensions of supports, Nr's 15 to 24 inclusive to drawing AP/3/041/b	300
2	Pipe Trench 4a Pipe Supports (drawing AP/3/041/a)	Alter size of bolt jigs, (pipe support nr 24 only)	50
	VARIATION ORDER		
		COST OF VARIATION	£ 350
		ESTIMATED COST (ORIGINAL ORDER)	£4200
		TOTAL EXPECTED COST (AMENDED)	£4550

Figure 8.4   small building works variation order

ABC CHEMICAL INDUSTRIES plc Head Office: Grangetown Refinery Grangetown G47 74G	COMPLETION CERTIFICATE	
	Order Nr: 25724	Project Ref: Nr 3 Acid Plant
	Date of Issue 4/1/92	Issued by: R. Smith
	Completion Date: 17/2/92	Variation Orders (if applicable) 1314

To: R. Black (Building Contractor)
       123, Redland Avenue
       Redland, Grangetown
 	
       Tel: 094 712 87327
	From: R. Smith (Superintendent)
	        D. Jones (Supervisor
	        Small Works)
	        Nr 3 Acid Plant
	
	        Tel: int 4144

Pipe Trench 4a, Pipe Supports
(North-South run, 24 nr)
drawings AP/3/041/a
             AP/3/041/b
v.o.   1314

Works Certified Complete:

Date: 18/2/92   R. Smith
                          (Works Superintendent)

Figure 8.5   small building works completion certificate

```
┌─────────────────────────────────────────────────────────────────────┐
│                  R. BLACK (BUILDING CONTRACTOR) plc                   │
│  Registered Office:                                                   │
│  123 Redland Avenue                                                   │
│  Redland                                                              │
│  Grangetown                              VAT Reg No: 12374214136      │
├──────────────────────────────┬──────────────────────────────────────┤
│  Client:                     │  Contract Ref: Nr 3 Acid Plant        │
│                              ├──────────────────────────────────────┤
│  ABC Chemical Industries     │  Contract Nr: 92/12                   │
│  Grangetown Refinery         ├──────────────────┬───────────────────┤
│  Grangetown                  │  Start Date:     │  Completion Date   │
│  G47 74G                     │  1/1/92          │  31/12/94          │
│                              ├──────────────────┼───────────────────┤
│                              │  Valuation Nr:   │  Date of Submission│
│                              │       2          │  7/3/92            │
├──────────────────────────────┴──────────────────┴───────────────────┤
│                                                                       │
│     Nr 3 Acid Plant                                                   │
│     Maintenance & Minor Capital Projects (Term Contract)             │
│     Valuation Nr: 2                                                   │
│                                                                       │
│                                                                       │
│       Works Orders:        previously measured          8000.00      │
│       Dayworks:            previously measured           100.00      │
│                                                                       │
│     Works Orders (this period):                                      │
│                                                                       │
│                    25751           1700.00                            │
│                    25722            200.00                            │
│                    25723            900.00                            │
│                    25724           4600.00                            │
│                    25725            175.00                            │
│                    25726            425.00                            │
│                                    8000.00                            │
│        Daywork (this period):        nil                              │
│                                    8000.00                            │
│                                                                       │
│                                                                       │
│     Details: see attached measures                                   │
│                                                                       │
│                                                                       │
│             TOTAL REQUESTED, VALUATION 2:       £ 8000.00             │
│                                                                       │
│             TOTAL MEASURED WORK TO DATE:       16 000.00             │
│             TOTAL DAYWORKS TO DATE:               100.00             │
│             TOTAL CONTRACT VALUE TO DATE:     £16 100.00             │
│                                                                       │
└─────────────────────────────────────────────────────────────────────┘
```

Figure 8.6   Contractor's small building works interim valuation summary

Appendix 2: Definition of Terms

This appendix presents the definition of terms relevant to the procurement, organisation and management of 'Small Building Works'. Where referenced, definitions are derived from known authoritative sources.

Annual term contract:

a term contract, on a measured or daywork rates basis, with a twelve month contract period used typically, though not exclusively, to procure a single trade or specialism. Often referred to as a single trade term contract.

'Buildability':

the extent to which the design of a building facilitates ease of construction, subject to the overall requirements of the completed building.

Daywork:

work undertaken on a cost reimbursement arrangement, based upon the number of operatives employed and the manhours expended. Sometimes referred to as a cost reimbursement or cost plus contract, since the contractor charges the client for the cost of labour, plant and materials plus an addition for overheads and profit.

Daywork order:

a written authorisation from the client to the contractor to undertake specific works on a daywork (cost reimbursement) basis.

Daywork term contract:

a term contract, typically three years in duration, under which a single contractor undertakes a series of works with payment authorised by the client on a daywork basis.

DIY building sector:

that proportion of total construction output accounted for by 'do it yourself' (DIY) labour supplied by householders or occupiers, quantified from the annual expenditure on DIY materials by householders.

Direct labour:

direct employment of the labour force as part of the client's (*employer's*) organisation. Often referred to as directly employed labour (DEL).

Estimated Annual Value (EAV):

the anticipated annual value of a term contract. Under term contracts, individual works may not be accurately specified, quantified or valued by the client but an anticipated value, the EAV, will be advised to the contractor for tendering purposes.

Estimated Contract Value (ECV):

similar to the estimated annual value (EAV), but specifies the anticipated total contract value. Specified for an annual term contract or specified for a term contract in addition to the EAV where there may be fluctuation in the EAV from year to year.

Foreman's order:

a type of works order issued by the client under a term contract to authorise specific works. In some cases a foreman's order is traditionally another name for works order and used in the same way.

Jobbing builder:

a builder/craft operative who undertakes jobbing works. Generally described as a semi-skilled operative who undertakes a wide variety of building trades/works. Is often likened to a builder's labourer who is also deemed a semi-skilled construction operative.

Jobbing works:

those works, carried out to instruction but without prior written quotation, without documentation and without formal arrangement between the client (*employer*) and builder (*craft operative*).

Lump sum contract:

a form of agreement or contract between the client and contractor where the contractor agrees to carry out the work for an agreed sum based upon information derived from drawings, specification and other relevant documentation. Clients may adopt an open or selective tendering strategy.

Measured term contract:

a form of agreement between the client and a single contractor in which a series of works of a similar and measured type and nature and which fall within specified cost parameters are carried out within the one contract and are measured and valued to a pre-determined schedule of rates.

Ordered works:

those works which are too large to adopt a jobbing approach yet are insufficiently large to justify the use of a standard shorter form of building contract, such as those used on small/minor building projects, but are works which require a structured approach to procurement and management and utilise documentation and a formal written agreement between the client and contractor.

Schedule of rates:

a pre-costed schedule of construction activities used for the measurement and valuation of works. Used predominantly on term contracts where the competitive element in tender bids is reflected in the different percentage price adjustments (mark-up) added, or deducted, as the case may be, by the tenderers.

Small building works:

any and all building works which are encapsulated in three defined groups: jobbing works; ordered works; and small/minor building projects.

Small/minor building projects:

those building works procured under a standard shorter form of building contract.

Works order:

a written authorisation from a client to a contractor to undertake specific works on a fixed price or measured basis. For individual small works, orders are issued on a fixed price basis whilst on term contracts measurement and valuation is undertaken to an agreed schedule of rates.

Appendix 3: Sources of Further Information

Building and Construction Industry statistics

Building Maintenance Information,
(A Company of the Royal Institution of Chartered Surveyors),
85–87 Clarence Street,
Kingston upon Thames,
Surrey, KT1 1RB.

National Economic Development Office (NEDO),
Millbank Tower,
Millbank,
London, SW1P 4QX.

Forms of contract

Department of the Environment (DoE),
Romney House,
43 Marsham Street,
London, SW1P 3PY.

(*General Conditions of Contract for Measured Term and Daywork Term arrangements*)

Institute of Registered Architects,
(*Architects & Surveyors Institute, Faculty of Architects and Surveyors*),
15 St Mary Street,
Chippenham,
Wilts, SN15 3JN.

(*FAS Small Works, Minor Works Contracts*)

Joint Contracts Tribunal (JCT)
Royal Institute of British Architects (RIBA),
66 Portland Place,
London, W1N 4AD.

Joint Contracts Tribunal (JCT),
RIBA Publications Ltd,
Finsbury Mission,
Moreland Street,
London EC1V 8VB.

(*JCT Agreement for Minor Building Works, JCT 80 MW*)

Property Services Agency (PSA),
Whitgift Centre,
Wellesley Road,
Croydon, Surrey, CR9 3LY.

Property Services Agency (PSA),
Directorate of Building and Quantity Surveying Services,
Apollo House,
Wellesley Road,
Croydon, Surrey, CR9 3RR.

(*General Conditions of Government Contract for Building and Civil Engineering Minor Works, GC/Works/2*)

Scottish Building Contract Committee (SBCC),
Secretary's Office,
39 Castle Street,
Edinburgh, 2.

Scottish Building Contract Committee (SBCC),
Publications Department,
15 Rutland Square,
Edinburgh, 1.

(*SBCC Form for Minor Building Works*)

Research

The following Governmental bodies, institutions and professional organisations undertake or promote research within many and varied fields of construction activity. Some research activities may be relevant to small building works procurement, contract organisation and management.

General

Building Research Establishment (BRE),
Garston,
Watford, Herts, WD2 7JR.

Chartered Institute of Building (CIOB),
Englemere,
Kings Ride,
Ascot, Berks, SL5 8BJ.

Construction Industry Research and Information Association (CIRIA),
6 Storey's Gate,
London, SW1P 3AU.

Department of the Environment (DoE),
Construction Industry Directorate,
Romney House,
43 Marsham Street,
London, SW1 3YP.

Royal Institution of Chartered Surveyors,
12 Great George Square,
Parliament Square,
London, SW1P 3AD.

Science and Engineering Research Council,
Secretariat,
Building Sub-Committee,
Polaris House,
North Star Avenue,
Swindon.

Specific

Department of the Environment (DoE), Science and Engineering Research Council (SERC),
Link Programme in Construction Maintenance and Refurbishment,
(Link CMR Programme, 1990–94),
Programme Co-ordinator, SERC,
Polaris House,
North Star Avenue,
Swindon.

(*Research Project: Management of Small Works and Minor Maintenance Projects, grant no: CMR Link 90h*

Schedule of rates

Standard schedules of rates for building works –

Property Services Agency (PSA),
Directorate of Building and Quantity Surveying Services,
Apollo House,
Wellesley Road,
Croydon, Surrey CR9 3RR.

Appendix 4: Select Bibliography

Bowyer, J., *Small Works Contract Documentation*. Architectural Press, (1976)

Building Maintenance Information, Measured Term Contracts BHI Special Report, serial 193, (1990)

Campbell, C.W., *The Management and Procurement of Small Works*. MSc. Degree thesis, Heriot-Watt University, (un-published), (1990)

Centre for Strategic Studies in Construction, University of Reading. *Building Britain 2001*, (1988),

Clamp, H., *The Shorter Forms of Building Contract*. Blackwell Scientific Publications, (1988)

Griffith, A., *Quality Assurance in Building*. Macmillan Press, (1990)

Harlow, P.A., *Managing Building Maintenance*. Chartered Institute of Building, (1985)

Harris, F. & McCaffer, R., *Modern Construction Management*. Granada, (1989)

Lee, R., *Building Maintenance Management*. Granada, (1987)

McNulty, A.P., *Management of Small Construction Projects*. McGraw Hill, (1982)

Milne, R.D., *Building Estate Maintenance Administration*. Spon, (1985)

Seeley, I.H., *Building Maintenance*. Macmillan Press, (1987)

Turner, A., *Building Procurement*. Macmillan Press, (1990)

Turner, D.F., *Building Contracts, A Practical Guide*. Longman, (1983)

Index